Effective
Technical Speeches
and Sessions

Effective Technical Speeches and Sessions

A GUIDE

FOR SPEAKERS AND PROGRAM CHAIRMEN

HOWARD H. MANKO

Director, Research and Development, Alpha Metals, Inc.

McGRAW-HILL BOOK COMPANY   *New York   St. Louis*
San Francisco   London   Sydney   Toronto   Mexico   Panama

EFFECTIVE TECHNICAL SPEECHES AND SESSIONS

39896

1234567890 MAMM 754321069

To my parents,
Whose many sacrifices put me on my way

How to Use This Book

This book was written to make the technical meeting more interesting and lively. As such, it covers the three major aspects required for a good technical meeting. These are in order of importance: the preparation of lively speeches, the organization of a successful technical meeting, and finally, the parliamentary procedures to keep any meeting orderly. The book, therefore, is divided into three sections, each one an entity in itself.

If you are interested in preparing a technical speech for delivery in someone else's program, Section I is for you. The chapters are designed to guide you through the various steps required to make your paper as interesting and lively as possible.

The temptation of giving a paper at a technical meeting whenever invited is a normal, human reaction. However, in order to avoid disappointments, it might be well to determine beforehand whether the paper is really worthwhile. Chapter 1 provides a self-evaluation outline which would help in predetermining whether the paper has a good chance of being well accepted by the audience. Therefore, if you have been invited to give a paper, and, after reading this chapter, you are convinced you definitely want to, it is time to evaluate the type and style desired. This is the subject of Chapter 2. Audience background and educational level, the type of society, organization of the paper, and other criteria are stressed. This helps assure good acceptance by the particular audience anticipated.

A successful technical presentation cannot be organized without a central "message." This determines the mood and the tone of the paper. This message should be considered as the only justification for giving the paper. Chapter 2 shows how this is used to help the potential speaker organize himself. A list of suggested messages to cover most occasions is also given.

A speech that runs overtime, or one that is too brief, can cause a speaker much aggravation. Hints are given on how to gauge the time allotted to match your paper to it. Chapter 2 also takes you through the stages of a dry run. A checklist will help you to evaluate your own work in practice sessions. To help in this task, a Correction Worksheet is also provided.

The actual mechanics of preparing a lively presentation are outlined in Chapter 3. The pitfalls of reading a paper are described and the need for preparing oral presentations to augment and round out the written material are stressed. The chapter then goes through the mechanics of preparing a title, one which will not mislead the audience. It analyzes the various segments of a speech: introduction to set the audience interest; the body of the speech, with some hints on the best way to present dry, technical data; and the importance of a strong conclusion.

The use of the right vocabulary for a presentation is another important aspect of the dynamic technical speech. Chapter 4 deals with vocabulary, which should not be impressive and understood by everyone. The chapter also has some hints on improving your word treasury and increasing it through simple practices. But above all, it stresses accurate expressions and easily understood words.

There are many ways of setting up technical presentations in an interesting form. Chapter 5 discusses these in detail, giving special attention to the "logical approach." This is the most common format for scientific papers. It gives some thought to "comparison" and "demonstration" and outlines the advantages of using the "negative approach"— a forceful way of bringing home your point. It also discusses somewhat more difficult forms of speech, such as ridicule and humorous presentation.

Many a speaker has had much heartache due to the improper use of jokes or poor storytelling techniques. This whole aspect is discussed in detail in Chapter 5. Some basic methods of matching the humorous story to the occasion are outlined. Some practical hints on good storytelling are also incorporated.

Another area which can cause much embarrassment to you as the speaker, is your personal introduction. Chapter 6 deals with that aspect. It will help you, as the speaker, maintain the proper dignity of the occasion. A Checklist, together with instructions on how to accept the introduction, is also given. Some hints on writing your own introduction complete this chapter.

Technical meetings today are seldom held without the profuse use of visual aids in the form of slides, films, and similar material. In order to make your own visual aids effective, Chapter 7 goes through the many details needed. Preparing your visual aids and also selecting what visual aids would be suitable for a particular occasion are discussed. The type of equipment you would require for any situation is also described. Some simple instructions for the proper preparation of artwork, etc., help simplify this task.

Instructions are given on the preparation of "lecture cards" which are a memory jog to the speaker. These must be coupled with the visual aids and become the best outline for your paper.

Finally, Chapter 8 discusses the speaker's manners—how to make certain they do not detract from his presentation, how to dress properly for the stage, what to do with his hands and feet, and so forth are covered. Some professional hints on eye contact, voice modulation, and the proper use of the lectern conclude this chapter.

To summarize Part 1, a checklist you should study before accepting a speaking assignment is given below (Exhibit 1). Certain points mentioned are keyed in with the various chapters.

Exhibit 1. Checklist before Accepting a Speech Assignment

   a. Do I want to show off? (Chapter 1)
   b. Do I have a message that is important? (Chapter 2)
   c. Is this the right audience for my subject? (Chapter 2)
   d. Can I make my talk interesting? (Chapters 3, 4, 5)
   e. Are visual aids practical? (Chapter 7)
   f. Do I have the time to prepare and practice?

After accepting the speaking assignment, Exhibit 2 is intended as a final checklist to see whether you are ready to get up and speak.

Exhibit 2. Checklist before Delivery of Talk

   a. Have I prepared my material well? (Chapter 3)
   b. Are the visual aids and lecture cards in order? (Chapter 7)
   c. Did I practice enough? (Chapter 8)
      1. Timing
      2. Appearance
      3. Voice
   d. How would I rate my talk?
      1. Would I like to listen to it?
      2. Would I recommend it to my friends?

With the help of these instructions, it should be easy to make adequate preparation for a most successful technical presentation at conventions, seminars, etc. It is suggested that you read the entire section before you start preparing your material. Once you have read through the material, it is then suggested that you go chapter-by-chapter, preparing your paper simultaneously to ensure the best success. And it is hoped that with these instructions the author has been able to put you well on your way to good technical speaking.

If you are assigned to organize a technical meeting by yourself or with a committee, Part 2 is written for you. Although many people attend technical meetings, few realize the enormous amount of effort that goes into their preparation. This is actually a thankless task since everybody is quick to complain but few will praise the organizers.

Chapter 9 provides a look behind the scenes of technical meetings and what is required to upgrade them. It bemoans the unhappy state of affairs that exists in many societies where little or no attention is given to the quality of papers accepted. A careful survey of this data will help you to avoid the mistakes others are making and help you to prepare an outstanding presentation that will bring you much credit. This chapter applies both to the program chairman and the speakers.

The last two chapters cover the organization of the meeting itself, and what a good master of ceremonies should know to run it smoothly. As you will discover, technical meetings don't have to follow the normal "sequential" pattern. There are many other stimulating forms such as panels, workshops, etc. Typical programs and some hints for the master of ceremonies should make this task easy. Part 2 also contains specific information on room setup, selection of locations, and the type of equipment required.

Part 3 was written and published separately by Mr. George Cavanaugh and is included in this book because it is an excellent guide to the intricacies of parliamentary procedure. Many a meeting will drag out unnecessarily because the people who are in charge are not familiar with the simple rules outlined in this section. Although the information therein seems complicated in the beginning, once you have gone through one or two meetings using these outlines, they will stay in your memory as the best shortcuts to efficient chairmanship.

The analysis of the motions—a vital part of meetings—is very thorough. So are the guidelines for committees. Once you read Chapter 13 you are sure to enjoy future committee participation as chairman or member. Should you find yourself in the minority, don't let that worry you. Chapter 15 was compiled to help you in this situation.

You might never start an organization of your own, but you are sure to belong to several technical societies. Chapter 16 delves into the basic rules required to govern the organization and the way it should be run. It provides an excellent insight into the setup, and makes it look easy.

Howard H. Manko

Additional Reading Material

A quick survey of technical societies for information they furnish to potential speakers yielded a number of acceptable sheets of instructions. Some of these are noted below. Should you be invited to give a paper by a society, it is suggested you contact it to see whether they have similar material that has been specifically prepared for your professional activities.

1. *American Chemical Society*: "Suggestions on How to Organize, Present and Illustrate a Technical Paper"
2. *I.E.E.E.*: "Techniques for Better Talks at the International Convention"
3. *American Society for Metals:* "The Oral Presentation of Technical Papers"
   "Instructions to Authors for the Preparation of Technical Papers"
   "ASM Speakers' Guide"
4. *American Society for Testing and Materials*: "Presentation of Technical Papers"
5. *Eastman Kodak Company* (for artwork only!):
   "Producing Slides and Filmstrips"
   "Effective Slide Lectures"
   " More Here's How"
   "Legibility Standards for Projected Material"
   "Artwork Size Standards for Projected Visuals"
   "Planning and Producing Visual Aids"
   "Basic Copying"

For those men who want to improve their ability in public speaking and communication through practice, there is Toastmasters International, a nonprofit organization of clubs which are dedicated to helping their members improve their abilities of leadership and communication. Clubs meet regularly in practically every major city in North America, plus 45 other countries of the free world.

The author owes this organization a great deal. It was the participation in the program—called Basic Training—that started me on the road to technical speaking. It gave me the foundation upon which to build my professional lectures. My certificate of merit in Basic Training from a Toastmasters club in Dugway, Utah, is a cherished possession.

In addition to communication and leadership training, the Toast-masters program offers men the opportunity to improve their conference and meeting techniques, listening abilities, and knowledge of parliamentary procedure. For further information about this world-wide organization write to Toastmasters International World Headquarters, 2200 North Grand Ave., Santa Ana, California, 92711.

Contents

The Speaker and the Speech

From studying the available literature, the reader should not get the impression that speechmaking is difficult. It is not necessary to be a showman or rhetorical expert in order to deliver a good paper. As Part 1 of this book will illustrate, all that is necessary is proper planning and thorough preparation.

To avoid giving a dull lecture, the speaker must understand his audience. He must know what they came to hear and learn. With this information in mind, he can readily prepare a stimulating lecture with the aid of many of the speech tools provided in the following pages.

Also necessary to an effective presentation is a definite message which will serve as the "nucleus" of the talk. The message helps the speaker to bring his ideas across to the audience and, at the same time, is essential for organizational purposes.

Once the planning stage is completed, the mechanics of preparing the speech are simple. The preparation of outlines, lecture cards, visual aids, etc., is described in detail later in this book. Checklists are also included for the reader's convenience.

It is during the actual preparation of the speech that stage fright usually sets in. This can readily be overcome in two ways: First, by polishing the presentation through many rehearsals and evaluations, and second, through a knowledge of the simple rules of public speaking and of what is expected of the speaker. Once you are familiar with the do's and don'ts of these, you will be able to come across well to your audience despite your fears. Understanding the problem is half the battle, and thorough preparation will enable you to be very effective in your speech.

In addition, you should remember that the audience has come voluntarily to listen to your paper. It has not come to be entertained, and therefore you do not have to be theatrically inclined. In this respect, engineers and scientists have a distinct advantage over others such as actors and politicians, for technical speakers are not judged by the quality of their performance alone. Unlike politicians, they rarely have to sell a point of view and/or themselves, and thus their task is far easier. They are usually judged by the quality of their work and speak to an audience which has come specifically to learn of their achievements.

Technical speakers have another advantage over actors because they are the authors and the creators of the material they are presenting and, therefore, are best qualified to interpret it. This is not so with actors, who must accurately interpret and present someone else's script.

The presentation of papers at technical meetings is the culmination of the scientist's and engineer's professional efforts. This is an aspect of technical work which is neglected in most universities. It is this phase of the work which Part 1 of this book covers in detail. This discussion is intended as an aid to both the novice and the experienced lecturer.

1 *So You Think You Have a Good Paper*

INTRODUCTION

Sooner or later, every professional is asked to give a technical presentation. It is one of those tasks for which he usually is not well trained at the university. Nevertheless, it is a required step in obtaining professional status both inside the organization and in the community. The rewards to be reaped from such technical presentations are many. Not only do they enhance your position, making advancement much easier, but they also help to familiarize people with the particular contributions that you have made in the field. They open channels of communication with other divisions or departments. They also provide a critical review of your work—a subject discussed in greater detail later on.

Giving a paper only for the sake of prestige is not recommended. It usually causes the speaker more consternation than satisfaction. This chapter is intended to help you determine whether you will have the effect that you desire. It is not meant to discourage you, but rather to help you make sure that your speech will not be a failure.

Be honest with yourself

Whenever you have the opportunity to present a paper, be honest with yourself. Ask yourself why you wish to give the speech and whether it is really worthwhile. It is important to note that a speech and a written

3

report serve very different purposes; the former is intended to update the audience's knowledge and to provide an overview of the subject, while the latter treats the subject in greater detail. Thus, a speech should never resemble a written report. (This point is developed in Chap. 3.)

All too often, people are motivated to give speeches only for the "glory" that they associate with speechmaking. This notion of the prestige of speaking before a group apparently stems from our having listened to a progression of parents and teachers since childhood. In any case, this imparts to lecturing a certain glamor which makes it difficult to resist.

Before you decide to give a speech, therefore, you should examine your motives for doing so. Do you have a real contribution to make, or do you simply wish to speak in order to show the audience how smart you are? Is the work you have been doing important? Do you really have a worthwhile subject? It must be pointed out here that there is no greater disappointment to the speaker than a poorly received presentation. This can hurt more than help in your professional development.

Though the foregoing seems discouraging, it was meant to be helpful. Honest evaluation of your motive for giving the paper is essential. The types of papers that are well accepted are discussed in detail in Chap. 2. If your paper meets these criteria, you need not be afraid that it will be a failure.

What your audience is looking for

In planning your talk, remember the audience that you are addressing. Make certain that you will be able to give them the information that they expect while you hold their interest. You should be able to impress them, not with yourself and your knowledge or the scope of your work, but with the information and the message that you have to offer.

The average listener is not really interested in the detailed mechanics of the material being presented. The setup of test equipment, procedures, and the correlation of information is of minor importance. He is really interested only in those aspects of your work which are relevant to his own field of endeavor. Thus, it is sometimes necessary for you to swallow your pride in the work that you have accomplished and to present a paper which does not dwell on its refinements.

Looking at your work from this point of view has many advantages. Foremost is the self-criticism that it provides. It may indicate to you the futility in pursuing certain avenues of approach. It will prevent you from spending your time in areas which, at second glance, seem trivial and unimportant. Also, many authors and researchers have admitted that the necessity for reporting their findings often helps them reappraise the work they have done and gives a new direction to future work. Such a review was brought to the author's attention recently. An engineer was requested to give a talk to the research and engineering staff of his company. In his report, he first briefly described the project and then summarized by concluding that "close scrutiny of the work results indicated the futility of the project." He recommended to management that this particular avenue of research be dropped and a different approach be developed. This unique situation prompted the author to discuss it with the speaker. The engineer admitted that it was a shock to him to find out how little he had been able to accomplish. He further asserted that it was the need to organize his results for the presentation that brought the matter to his attention. He felt that without it he would have continued his futile effort. Needless to say, the work subsequently carried out by this individual was extremely successful. This story then illustrates one benefit of writing and presenting engineering and scientific material.

Types of talks that are well received

You have now looked into your motivation for giving your speech. You have established the suitability of the subject for your audience and have decided to proceed. It is time to briefly review some of the reasons that people would want to come to hear your presentation. It is difficult to cover all possible motivations, but the following are some of the major considerations which help to classify technical presentations.

Most people are interested in staying abreast of the latest developments in their field. Your work in a particular area makes you an expert on that subject. You are in a position to summarize both your own contributions and those of others and thus to update your listeners' knowledge as to the latest developments. If this is the aim of your presentation, the rewards are many. Normally, such a presentation results in a most stimulating discussion and question-and-answer period after the speech, and in a large request for reprints of your published work and for further details.

This updating can be subdivided into the following major categories:
1. State of art for new and established technologies.
2. New areas developing in a particular field of science or engineering.

3. A new theoretical treatment of an area of great technological interest.

Many people feel that this type of presentation is not original enough to be worth the effort involved. Yet it is a very well-received type of speech which is interesting to a large cross section of people. It most certainly helps to enhance your status and does not reflect on the originality of your work.

Another type of paper that is well received is a more specific treatment of new inventions, theories, or other developments. The subject is described to the audience with great emphasis on possible applications and areas of utilization. The speaker must never elaborate on work details or data correlation, however impressive they may be. This type of paper is straightforward, but it must be generalized and informative. This will make the presentation attractive to the audience.

Papers on existing manufacturing principles and descriptions of large assembly lines are also surprisingly well received by the audience. The information may seem to be commonplace to the speaker, since he is intimately involved with these operations on a daily basis, but this does not mean that it will not still be very interesting to the rest of the audience. Obtaining the company's permission is, of course, the biggest obstacle to giving this type of paper. However, large and small corporations have found it very advantageous to grant permission since it helps to enhance their image. It also indicates to potential customers the levels of technology which they have achieved. These papers are most impressive when they center around a simple concept. These might range from the degree of automation possible to obtaining quality from specific schemes, or possibly the application of specific scientific principles to the production line.

The final type of paper of great interest is the historical review. This is usually a presentation of non-original work based on the compilation of many other papers. Although the paper is not necessarily relevant to today's state of the art, it can be interesting and well received. Its message usually centers around "how we arrived where we are."

Now it is time for you to look at your own presentation to determine why you would come to hear it. In addition, you should consider whether it is worthy of being repeated before additional groups as a result of recommendations made by your audience. Remember, you have accomplished the hard work of preparing your talk and want to get maximum exposure by repeating it.

In summary, most audiences prefer to listen to a generalized treatment of a subject. They want to update their own knowledge and to see how the speaker's work applies to their problems. In general, they want to improve themselves. Your talk, therefore, should not emphasize specifics; these should be made available in written reports. If you address yourself to the general interests of your listeners, you should be successful.

Acceptance of a paper is no guarantee of quality

In many cases, the inexperienced speaker relies too heavily on the judgment of those involved in the administration and organization of conventions and technical meetings. Since they have accepted his paper for presentation, he feels certain that it will be well received by the audience and will thus lead him to fame and glory. But this is a misconception (see "The Story of a Hoax" on p. 88). Also, the basic difference between a speech and a written report should be kept in mind.

Conclusion

If the foregoing questions can be honestly answered in your favor, you should consider yourself ready to prepare a speech. The technique of perfecting a talk is described in the following chapters. You should be sure, though, that you do not lose sight of the basic considerations presented in this chapter as you proceed with the preparations.

2 Preparing an Interesting Paper

INTRODUCTION

This chapter considers those factors which make the difference between a dull technical presentation and a lively talk. A lively talk results not from any particular theatrical effect but usually from the proper planning and especially the development of a specific message, along with a dynamic method of presentation. When you consider giving a speech in a technical program, you must consider all of the points raised in the previous chapter. If you accept the challenge to give the paper, be sure that it is worth giving. Consider the mechanics of making such a paper interesting—and not only interesting, but also appropriate to the subject of the program and for the amount of time allotted. Preparation of a speech is an important task which requires much effort and which will greatly influence the quality of the presentation itself.

Analyzing your audience interest

The first and most important step in planning a technical presentation is a thorough analysis of the audience and its level of interest. You must avoid a basic mismatch between the audience's interests and the type of material presented. It is very disappointing to deliver a well-prepared paper to a group that is uninterested.

To be effective in your presentation, you must be aware of the audience's background and interests. It is important to know whether they are on the same educational level as yourself or less so. You must establish whether they are familiar with your subject or are only interested in learning some basic generalities about it. And, finally, you must find out how much they can absorb at the specific time of the day and during the amount of time scheduled for your lecture.

This information is readily available from the people who have organized the meeting. They know whom they are expecting and why they will come. You must not be disappointed if you are expected to aim your talk at a lower level than you are accustomed to; also, a condescending attitude on your part will not help to bring the point across. Remember that your aim is not to show off your own technical capabilities. You should always come down to the level of your listeners and never attempt to pull them up to yours. In most cases, only a small fraction of the audience will be really familiar with your particular area of endeavor. Seldom, therefore, will they be interested in a serious discussion of the unique contribution of your work. To satisfy the small number of experts in the audience, however, you should try to work up a series of conclusions and recommendations which would highlight your achievements in that area. Your published paper will supplement this information for them.

It is important to remember that no scientist or engineer can ever claim to have developed a scientific field singlehandedly, without the aid of predecessors who may, in one way or another, have contributed substantially to his thinking. It is therefore always advisable to list or credit some of the work of other people in related or preceding areas of development. It would be in poor taste to claim credit for all of your work since it is seldom, if ever, possible to achieve such results with one's own powers alone. In other words, be humble. You gain recognition and prestige from the fact that you have been invited to lecture and that your audience has come to listen to you.

Once you have analyzed the type of audience that you will be addressing, you should consider the appropriateness of your paper for this presentation. You may have to address nontechnical people or an audience unacquainted with your specialty. This could require a complete rearrangement of your material. On the other hand, you should not rule out the possibility of having to cover a subject in detail and according to some guidelines imposed by the technical society. In any situation, you are assured of success if you tailor your presentation to your audience's needs and interests.

By now you should have established exactly what your audience will want to hear, the depth of the scientific treatment necessary, and possible length and other details which will be valuable to them. Summarized in Fig. 2-1 are the various levels and types of audience interest that you should consider.

Figure 2-1 Setting the Tone of Your Paper

1. General interest in subject
    a. No details
    b. Some specifics
    c. Very explicit
2. Updating of topic area
3. Recent developments
4. Original material—highly technical
5. Application of knowledge to other fields
6. Do's and Don'ts in everyday practice
7. Case histories
8. Literature surveys or historical reviews

An analysis of many poor papers reveals that their defects stem from lack of awareness of the type of presentation that is really needed. Keeping both your audience and the appropriate type of presentation in mind, you are now ready to move to the next stage—that of developing the message.

Developing the message

Every engineering and scientific paper should have a message. This sounds rather ambitious, especially if the term "message" is not properly explained. A message can best be defined as the theme of the speech. It is the "why" of the talk and, as such, should be clearly stated right at the beginning. It helps to hold the audience's attention by telling them the purpose of the lecture. It evokes curiosity about the subject in the listener. Even more important to the speaker is the guidance that the message provides. It serves as a thread running through his thoughts and helps to keep the talk to the point.

At first glance it might appear that there is no room for real messages in most engineering and scientific papers. The information to be presented does not appear to lend itself to this type of treatment. However, you must remember that it is difficult to generate real audience interest without finding one specific idea around which to build the paper. The paper must, therefore, have a message in the interest of continuity and to retain the audience's interest.

Ideas for messages are many. They might be as simple as an appeal to continue working in a specific direction started by the speaker. Or they may be more sophisticated, for example, in the form of a request for assistance from the audience to put a new idea or theory into practice. Sometimes you might want to address yourself to "reliability or economy through the use of new techniques." A scientist may want to have his colleagues keep him informed of their own findings to confirm or refute a theory that he has advanced. The simplest of all messages are provided by literature surveys and the chronological treatments of developments in a field.

Finding the message is not really as difficult as it might seem at first glance. The message is easily developed from analysis of the audience and from intimate knowledge of one's own material. A paper does not have to limit itself to a single message. However, more than three messages is usually not recommended unless they tie in with each other.

Remember that once you have a message it should be used continuously throughout the entire discussion; the paper should be built around the message in such a manner that there will be no doubt in the minds of the listeners as to what your aims are.

It is doubtful that you can present an interesting paper that will hold the audience's interest without a central theme. To resume our analogy with the artist in the play, the message can be compared to the theme. Without a definite and interesting plot around which the play revolves, the artist (even with the best of delivery and theatrical ability) will have a bored audience watching his performance.

Setting the mood for your paper

The message that you have selected will enable you to set the mood for your paper. Although enthusiasm is the most important part of the actual delivery of a speech, and a speech should never be given without it, the paper itself can have in addition a more particular mood.

The most effective mood depends on the type of message that you develop. A paper presented without emotion will catch little of the audience's fancy. Scientific papers seldom lend themselves to happy and joyous moods unless they are straightforward success stories. On the other hand, the whimsical approach coupled with a joyous, light-hearted, and humorous attitude can often lead to an effective means of presentation.

In general, scientific and engineering papers lend themselves more to the angry or reproachful type of attitude in the vein of "if you don't do this, you will be sorry," or "I can't understand why people fail to see the reason for doing such-and-such." An angry speaker can put across his point more effectively than others, especially if he believes thoroughly in his own message. A more complete list of moods is given here:

1. Happy
2. Lighthearted or humorous
3. Whimsical
4. Angry or reproachful
5. Glum
6. Solemn
7. Warning (campaign style)
8. Pleading

One important word of advice. The speaker must be convinced of his message and must assume the mood that really fits his own ideas, or he will never sound convincing to his audience. A half-hearted message presented by a speaker whose attitude is not really genuine will be condemned by the audience and the talk will be a failure.

As you can see, mood is an additional tool which can give your talk color. If this is your first paper, don't shy away from whatever mood you think appropriate. Discuss it with a friend if you feel that it is difficult or unnatural for you to maintain. After several rehearsals you will find it to be of tremendous benefit and thereafter you will never attempt to speak without first selecting a mood.

Gauging the time allotted

Now that you are ready to plunge into the actual preparation, it is still necessary to decide how much of the material that you wanted to include really fits within the framework of the time allotted. Don't attempt to cram too much into your presentation. Only the material that can be delivered in proper fashion in the given amount of time should be included, or you will lose the effectiveness that you seek.

Once again, you must take a hard look at what the audience wants. After you have drawn an outline you might have to cut back on the material in order to stay within the limits of your talk. It is best to select the major aspects of your talk and to elaborate on them. Give sufficient detail to convey your message. Never try to present too much material in too short a time, however. Running overtime and/or rambling on and on will not contribute to your image. In general, you will find it difficult to squeeze all of your material in. You should trim it down to fit the occasion.

This, once again, indicates the importance of conveying a message rather than trying to impress your audience. Remember that by being selected for the presentation, you have already been paid the compliment of being considered an expert in your field. It is on the effectiveness of your speech that your audience is going to judge you.

Preparing the paper itself

The next few chapters are designed to help you in transforming your paper into a lively presentation. Chapter 3 deals with the specific elements necessary for a good paper and Chap. 4 with the vocabulary that you should be using. Chapter 5 is designed to explain the various tools available to the speaker which help to develop the message as well as to establish the mood. Finally, Chap. 7 helps in the preparation of visual aids, and Chap. 8 treats speaker mannerisms.

Figure 2-2   Worksheet

```
 1.  Title of paper
 2.  Time, place, society, etc.
 3.  Audience interest and size
 4.  The message and the mood
 5.  Time allotted
 6.  Outline with details
 7.  Visual aids
 8.  Practice
 9.  Self-evaluation
10.  Dry run
```

It is suggested that you start out by making a worksheet for yourself according to Fig. 2-2.

You should make a rough outline first. Match this outline to the information given in the next few chapters. This will help you in considering the various points raised in this chapter. Once you are sure of what you really want, it is time to prepare the paper itself. Many people write out their speech beforehand, though this is a relatively dangerous practice. It is difficult to remember the written words exactly. In addition, people have a tendency to write in a different manner than that in which they speak. However, do write down your key sentences and elaborate on them in your practice speeches and in the final presentation. In this respect, the preparation of lecture cards with or without visual aids is indispensable (see p. 71).

Practice makes perfect

Chapter 8 is intended to aid the speaker in developing the right mannerisms, eye contact with the audience, voice modulation, and the use of other mechanical devices that help to polish his performance. However, reading this chapter is no substitute for actual practice. It is doubtful that any public speaker can effectively present a paper without adequate rehearsal. The amount of time and effort that is required varies with the individual; it depends on how experienced a speaker the person is and on how familiar he is with the material that he is covering.

Rehearsing a speech today is no longer as difficult as it was in the time of Demosthenes,[1] who is said to have had serious physical handicaps which made public speaking virtually impossible. He reportedly overcame his faulty enunciation and voice projection by such means as holding pebbles in his mouth while he spoke, practicing in front of a mirror, and projecting his voice over the roar of the waves hitting the rocks on the beach. With the miracle of today's electronics and audio systems, poor voice projection and similar difficulties can be compensated for with the proper use of the microphone (see p. 81).

However, the speaker must still prepare himself thoroughly, using a mirror and possibly a tape recorder in his rehearsal. It has often been noted that a man is his own best critic. You can help to improve your technique by close scrutiny of your own rehearsals. Listening to a tape recording, especially several days later, helps you pick out the defects in your presentation.

Let us all remember that great speakers, even when they seem to be speaking impromptu, really have put in considerable effort beforehand.

---

[1] Athenian orator and statesman, 384?-322 B.C.

The story is told that Winston Churchill had actually prepared himself well in advance for the eventuality of giving a victory speech after World War II, and thus when the time came, his "impromptu" Berlin oratory did not disappoint his listeners.

The late President Kennedy also rehearsed his famous inaugural address, which included such stirring words as "In the long history of the world, only a few generations have been granted the role of defending freedom in an hour of maximum danger. I do not shrink from this responsibility, I welcome it. And so, my fellow Americans, ask not what your country can do for you; ask what you can do for your country."

Evaluating your speech

Once you have completed the preparation and rehearsal of your speech, you should set up a dry run for your friends and colleagues. In an informal session, deliver your paper and ask them for their criticism. You should request that they be frank and comment to you on the various items about which you are concerned. The informal dry runs should be handled as if they were the real speech. You should select a location resembling the lecture hall in which the speech will be given. If

Figure 2-3   Criticism Worksheet

Note: Please do not judge the dry run on its technical content, since that is not the purpose of this criticism. If you have any thoughts in that respect, give them to the speaker in writing separately.

1. Is the speaker well prepared?
2. Did you get his message right from the start and did he make his point in the conclusion?
3. Were there specific areas of the talk that could cause confusion?
4. Was the talk interesting to you?
5. Were the visual aids appropriate?
6. Did any of the speaker's mannerisms detract from the effectiveness of his talk?[1]
7. What would you have done differently?
8. Did he stay within the time limits permitted?

[1] Do not expect the speaker to act too formally. He should act naturally and seem relatively at ease and refrain from any nervous behavior which might distract his audience.

possible, practice speaking through a microphone. Figure 2-3 contains a list of items which you might have your audience keep in mind while they listen to your presentation.

Conclusion

The dynamic technical presentation, like many other achievements, is the result of much preparation. In this chapter, a step-by-step procedure to help you prepare to give a successful presentation before a live audience has been outlined. When you become an experienced speaker, you will develop a style all your own. Until then, be sure that you have overlooked none of these points. There is nothing more discouraging than a disenchanted audience after you have put great effort into the preparation of your speech.

3 Transforming the Factual Paper into a Lively Presentation

By way of introduction: never read your paper

The novice might try to bolster his confidence by preparing his speech in detail at his desk, intending to read it later in front of his audience. In this way he hopes to avoid difficulties, and yet if you have ever attended a technical meeting, you know that the papers that are read are the most boring of the proceedings. This is easy to understand, since the written and spoken languages are very different. You can use a very correct and formal English when you write a composition or technical treatise, but this is not the same smooth flowing and readily understandable English that is used in speaking.

It is undesirable to read your report to the audience for another reason. A written technical paper requires a lot of detailed explanation and data that is important. Your scientific contribution is intended for people who will rely on it and keeping working from this material. As indicated in Chap. 2, the reading of such a manuscript is not of interest to your listeners. The material you really want to present to your audience must be more stimulating. Remember the message that we discussed which has to be the thread running throughout your speech. In order to make your speech lively, you must add life to that message. In addition, the allotted time in most meetings does not even permit discussing the work seriously.

Reading a speech, however, is an important part of the preparation of a formal manuscript. You should first sit down and write a paper. This is actually required for the technical proceedings or publications associated with most technical meetings. You should then try to make your speech a supplement to that written report. This is a practice that the author highly recommends to the reader.

Always make sure that your oral presentation is entirely different from your written report. This will make your audience want to listen to you and later to obtain reprints of your formal paper. Many technical societies today insist that this be so.

Only when it is necessary to present someone else's paper because of his illness or other circumstances are you justified in reading it. Your own paper should be delivered, rather than read. Reading your own work indicates a certain lack of preparation on your part. If you must read someone else's paper, read it well. The art of reading a paper aloud is one that few people have mastered. It requires a large amount of time in preparation, just as the studying of a script by an actor is time-consuming. Read it aloud many times, so that it will sound fluent and pleasant to the audience. Make sure that you maintain eye contact with the audience and do not resort to simply mumbling into the microphone. In short, be prepared. Remember that both your own and the author's reputations are at stake.

Keeping these guidelines in mind, let us go through a step-by-step preparation of the major items in a good talk. It is suggested that you follow this format rigidly, until you are able to develop a different style of your own.

Seeking the right title for a paper

The choice of a title for a paper is often disappointing to the author. A title must be brief and yet self-explanatory, and this is often difficult to achieve for a scientific or engineering presentation. A paper should have a nice, catchy title to attract audience interest. However, it should also have a subtitle giving the content of the paper in more detail. A short, nondescriptive name might very well cause disappointment to the audience. They may have been misled to believe that the subject would cover an entirely different area. In addition, this could cause audience distraction when some people leave the room as soon as the real purpose of the speaker is revealed. A subtitle for the paper, therefore, usually meets the necessity of expanding a title. It will show exactly which facet of the subject the speaker will address himself to. Furthermore, you are then at liberty to create a shorter, catchy title for the main title of the paper.

For example, if the contents of this chapter were to serve as the basis for a paper, the title should really represent the material. Just calling it "Effective Speaking," though this is catchy, would be misleading, since salesmen or politicians will not really find it appropriate. "Effective Technical Speaking" would also be misleading since this chapter does not help the scientist or engineer in the problems of daily professional communications. Therefore, an additional subtitle such as "Effective Speaking When Presenting Technical Papers" or "The Dynamic Presentation of Dry Technical Papers" is necessary.

There is a common misconception that it is advantageous to try to attract a large audience through a paper's title. This is usually an effort to make as wide an impression as possible. Actually, this backfires since people will have the wrong attitude. They will complain that they have been lured under false pretenses, that the material was not aimed at them. Either way, neither the lecturer nor the organizers of the meeting benefit from the experience.

A final remark as to when a title should be selected. The author has found it extremely difficult to select a title first and then to fit a presentation to it. It is more expedient to prepare the speech first and then to find the right title for the presentation. Usually, a condensed form of the message makes the best title.

An exciting introduction sets the pace

As any experienced speaker knows, the opening remarks (referred to here as "introduction") help determine the successfulness of a presentation. This should not be confused with the "personal introduction," which is discussed in Chap. 6. There is a common misconception that it is up to the speaker to open his talk with a joke. This is intended to put the audience in the right frame of mind. This is not true in the case of technical and engineering presentations. Most engineers and scientists are poor storytellers and, therefore, by telling a joke they hurt the purpose of their presentations rather than enhance it. It is also difficult to find a joke that is really appropriate to the message of the presentation. Unless one is schooled in using a joke to bring his audience's attention to focus on the message, it is strongly suggested that the use of such material be completely disregarded. For further information on the proper use of humor, see Chap. 5.

Your opening remarks should include a restatement of the paper's title and its intention. It is appropriate in the opening remarks to acquaint the audience with your message by stating it clearly. This should be coupled with a brief reference to the timeliness of the subject and its contemporary value. Your message will be much better appreciated and will seem far more impressive if its role in the overall scheme is clearly defined. This also serves in a most elegant but indirect way to increase your prestige as a speaker.

This part of the introduction should take between three and ten minutes, depending on the total time allotted to you. It must be preplanned with the conclusion in mind, for it should later be complemented by the conclusion. In many cases, this will be the part best remembered by your audience. A very careful preparation and rehearsal of the statement of the message is, therefore, to be considered a major part of the effort in preparing a speech.

Finally, in a few, well-chosen words it is necessary to outline to the audience exactly what your presentation consists of and how you anticipate bringing the message to them. You should explain the type of data and other material that you want to include in your presentation. Thus, a properly prepared introduction puts the audience in the correct, attentive mood. In addition, because you have clearly defined the material, they will be able to follow your lecture more readily.

If you have never written an introduction, here is a simple format which you may wish to use the first time.

1. Open by a restatement of your title and expand on the subtitle, if any. This should serve to clarify exactly what your paper is all about.

2. Follow by stating your message clearly. This is the most important part of the introduction.

3. Proceed from there to describe the contemporary value of your presentation.

4. Continue with a brief outline of the various subjects to be covered in the paper—here you can actually describe the various items that you are going to discuss, e.g., test equipment and procedures, graphs, results, etc.

5. Finish your introduction by stating the conclusion or restating the message.

In some cases, it is also a good idea to give the reason that the paper was prepared in the first place and why it is being presented to the particular assembly. If the subject seems extremely common, it might be wise to explain the uniqueness of the approach taken.

The body of your speech

The body of the speech depends on the subject and here the individual is the best judge of what should be covered. The organization of the paper is very important and, therefore, a clear outline must be prepared before the paper itself is written. Furthermore, remember that the data and other information presented must be meaningful and not too elaborate, otherwise the audience will be put to sleep. Here, a careful review of the next few papers dealing with the presentation of the technical data will be helpful. Finally, remember that it is up to you, the speaker, to interpret the results for the audience. Translate them into general terms and elaborate on the possibilities they open for future investigation. etc.

All through the body of the speech it is essential to continuously keep the message in mind and to touch on all those aspects which amplify and clarify it. The message can also be used as an excellent yardstick by which to determine which parts of the presentation are really meaningful and which might involve tedious details which are not of general interest. Again you must be warned to stay away from details which might impart to the audience the impression that you are there to impress them. You must realize that your biggest contribution is made and the most gratifying results obtained when you help the audience assimilate your message. That way you will obtain prestige without trying to impress them with your mental capacity.

The body of the speech is the one part which you as a scientist or engineer are best qualified to develop. There is no unique requirement here which would make it difficult for you to prepare. Follow the normal rules and practices for report writing that have been outlined for you during your technical training. It is just that particular emphasis must be placed on the message. In Chap. 4, the author goes into a detailed discussion of the vocabulary to be employed. Chapter 5 describes various tools of speech which help to increase the listener's interest in the material. It is suggested that you prepare the body of your speech in outline form now. Later, after reviewing these additional chapters, write in the details if you wish. Since the author does not advocate the reading of a paper, you can prepare the body of the speech in writing for practice only. This should be in simple English; you should not be encumbered at this time with the added chores of vocabulary choice. Later, when you select a form of speech which might be more dramatic or more entertaining, you should work out more specific details (see futher on in this chapter).

A discussion dealing with the preparation of the body of the speech without an indication of how to present dry technical data in an entertaining form would not be complete. Therefore, let us discuss it in detail.

Presenting dry data in a fascinating manner

In many cases the whole reason for the existence of scientific and engineering papers is the data that has been accumulated and which is now shared with the audience. A thorough discussion of the pertinent data in a pleasant capsule form is our aim. Yet, the technical data, in many cases, turns out to be the pitfall of the untrained speaker. Data presented from the podium without any particular selectivity can lead to great confusion. It is relatively difficult for one who is not very close to a particular discipline to assimilate data merely by listening to the speaker. Figures and statistical evaluations should never be presented by themselves without the use of visual aids or helpful preprints (for additional information on this subject, see Chap. 7).

Occasional figures and maps can be interspersed in the speech without any special difficulties. However, a large quantity of numbers, figures, and data is badly digested by most people and, therefore, must be avoided.

Too much variety, by itself, will give the paper no special advantage. The interesting oral presentation revolves around a message rather than the data, and thus differs from the written paper. A simple rule of thumb here is to present enough data in the speech to make the audience want to read the paper. In most cases, it will be available in the transactions or some other publication. It would be entirely permissible to mention only various areas that have been thoroughly investigated without submitting any particular data. You can then concentrate your efforts on several of the more important conclusions that can be derived from the work. These would be of general interest to the audience. The individual who might seek the more detailed information should be invited to see you after the presentation for a discussion of the facts and figures.

If it is absolutely necessary that you discuss a set of data and figures in order to make your message clear, you must use visual aids. These must be carefully prepared, not in quantities of abstract numerals, but in the form of simple bar graphs or similar graphic forms. Visual aids designed to make the assimilation of facts and figures easy for the general audience are covered in detail in Chap. 7. In addition, handing out some of the data as a preprint when it is absolutely necessary can also be arranged.

It is possible that this section of the chapter should have been entitled, "Why Data Should Not Be Presented in a Technical Speech." The point must be reemphasized that the value of data in oral presentations is, at best, limited. In order to maintain high audience interest, a figure should only be referred to, rather than presented. It is the message which is the core of the presentation. The data should serve to illustrate it rather than forming the focus of attention itself. Therefore, whenever you prepare a speech, view the data as the worst part of your presentation. It is more likely to bore your audience than to interest them. However, the conclusions which can be drawn from your data should be made a vital part of the presentation. Obviously, the data is necessary as documentation for your conclusions.

The conclusion

A powerful conclusion, like a good introduction, will help you be remembered. This, then, must be your aim when you prepare your summation remarks. In the conclusion you must repeat your opening statements and your message. In retrospect, you should have fired your audience's imagination with your introduction, maintained their interest throughout the body of the speech with your message, and now, in the conclusion, you must attempt to really make the sale. A good speaker who can end on this note is usually the speaker who is invited over and over again to give either the same speech or similar ones.

As your proficiency in public speaking increases, you will find it easier to relax while you are making your presentation. Then you will observe the audience and its reaction. It has been the writer's experience that it is very easy to catch the mood of the audience. It is easy to recognize subjects that heighten their interest, and these are easily amplified throughout the presentation. Those subjects which leave the audience cold are also obvious, and these should be deemphasized as the paper progresses. During the conclusion an alert speaker can touch on all those highlights which seemed to interest the audience. In this way, you make your paper and the conclusion accommodate the audience's interests to an even greater degree. This technique should not confuse the beginner, who may want to be a little more formal. If your speech has been well rehearsed and this particular point has been kept in mind, it is possible to prepare beforehand several statements which may or may not be used during the conclusion.

To derive all of these benefits from the conclusion, make sure that you do not exceed the time that you have been allotted. Only too often the speaker is asked to finish his presentation when the time has run out, before he has had a chance to draw his conclusions. It is, therefore, recommended that you prepare a slightly shorter paper, making sure that there is time for the conclusion, and then for opening the floor for a discussion and question-and-answer period. This is better than trying to fill out every minute of the presentation with material and possibly ending up with an incomplete conclusion.

Make yourself a typical outline first

Now that you have considered the major parts of a speech, it is recommended that you polish the final outline (see p. 13). This outline

Figure 3-1 Checking Out Your Paper

The checklist below is designed to help you ensure that your speech will be successful.

1. Is your title correct?
    a. Does it describe the material?
    b. Could it mislead the audience?
2. Do you have a "message"?
3. Is your introduction exciting?
4. Is your data easy to digest?
    a. Do you have visual aids?
    b. Could some data be simplified?
5. Is your conclusion perfected?
6. Have you practiced enough?
    a. Is your timing good?
    b. Have you had a dry run?

might consist of ten or twelve individual statements. The outline preparation will give you a general idea of the way your speech will progress. Each detail can be filled in later on. Once the outline is ready, it is necessary to evaluate each part according to the guidelines given in this book. Make sure that all parts will be of great interest to the audience and will help to bring the message across.

Filling in the details of the outline is a relatively easy task. This should again be done in a sketchy form which is not meant to be read, since you should never read your speech. Filling in the details really involves the preparation of a suboutline for yourself which you can use later on. Here you might find the preparation of lecture cards, as described in Chap. 7, extremely helpful. You should seldom go beyond the detail included on the lecture cards. Remember, the subject is well known to you and filling in the minor points in too much detail during this stage should be unnecessary.

It is now time to check out your paper to make sure that you have omitted nothing and to prepare yourself for the dry run and for the actual speech.

4 Using the Right Vocabulary Is Important

Vocabulary must be informative, not impressive

The secret of communication—really effective communication—is the use of vocabulary which is understood by all. Once this basic truth is considered, we immediately realize that the powers of persuasion (and, after all, we *are* trying to persuade the listener) are limited by the degree to which the audience understands the spoken words. If we employ words which are outside the realm of their everyday speech, the whole effect of the presentation is lost.

It is a human trait to try to impress others with our wisdom and knowledge. This includes the use of multisyllabic words which might sound impressive. This tendency to show off actually defeats the purpose of speech. Unless you address an audience that really understands the terms used, you may as well address the walls. It is also true that when such words are used the sentence structure is usually cumbersome and sounds artificial. This might cause subconscious rejection of the contents of the lecture. When you read or listen to famous people who address political parties or engineering societies, you seldom find them using impressive phrases. Here the simplicity of the speech often contributes to its beauty. As long as you have a real message to deliver, be it scientific or otherwise, the message and the knowledge displayed rather than the vocabulary will determine its effectiveness.

In a person's development, especially that of the scientist and engineer, great emphasis is laid on the accuracy of communication. In school, you are expected to measure up to the standards of your teachers and professors. Once you leave the confines of college, you are able to develop a style of your own, but it is still important for you to translate your thoughts as clearly as possible into words. You must use words that will convey your thoughts easily and accurately to your reader or your audience. They may be sophisticated, but they usually are not. The most important part of this process is selection of the right terms with which to express an idea. In addition, you should always be concise in your presentation and explanation of ideas.

The author is not advocating the use of a limited vocabulary. Everyone skilled in the minimum requirements of writing knows that it is essential to avoid the use of the same term over and over again. However, when a dictionary or thesaurus is consulted for additional terms, you will be wise to select the more commonly known rather than the obscure terms. This will best get your thought across to the average listener. In some cases it is necessary to coin phrases and to explain them for the benefit of the audience. A good speaker will often use common words for this purpose and will thus be able to express ideas concisely but fully.

Let us review a scientific essay where it is mandatory to define the terms. Here, unless a basic ground is laid for the use of scientific nomenclature, great confusion in communication can result. This is certainly true for all scientific work and this permits the introduction of refined vocabulary. In everyday life, however, or in a semitechnical discussion you should never define every concept and phrase you use. Such elaboration will not only insult your audience but make the speech most tedious and difficult. Therefore, the use of new, complicated words with or without explanation should be avoided.

Remember that flowery and complex English does not sell ideas. Unless your ear is attuned to such language, it requires more than normal concentration just to understand it. It also causes resentment on the part of the audience. Therefore, talk to your audience in their language and you will achieve the results that you have set out to attain. Above all, be sure to use the right word for the right idea and if you don't have a message to convey, don't get up to speak at all.

Substituting the message for elaborate vocabulary

As indicated in many other sections of the book, one of the secrets of success for any technical presentation is enthusiasm. If you concentrate on the message and follow it throughout the presentation as the main theme with honest conviction, you will easily get it across to your audience. A speaker who adopts this method soon loses himself in the presentation and has no time to search for those elusive, impressive words. Many experienced speakers report that when the audience is receptive and the conditions are right, they get carried away with the spirit of the occasion and get their ideas to the listeners without the processes that are so closely connected with the careful choice of words. Here, the use of precise, everyday language gives the best results. In order to prepare for this type of speech, it is necessary, of course, to practice year in and year out. The golden rule of speech is: Use the correct words to convey each idea; never take it for granted that your listener knows what you are talking about. You should not deviate from these standards in everyday speech. Such habits as poor word selection and improper sentence structure must be eliminated. The attitude that "you know what I am talking about and therefore correct definition is not required" should be discarded. A continuous, conscious effort must be made to make sure that in every conversation this process of word selection is followed. Your conversational ability should measure up to the same high standards as your speechmaking ability.

With these easy rules, then, the matter of selecting the proper vocabulary for a speech is considerably simplified.

Improving your vocabulary

After you embark on a career of public speaking, it is well worth developing your vocabulary. Unfortunately, the average scientist or engineer does not even master all of the simple words. Up to now in this chapter, the author has advocated the use of simple language in order to convey the message. This does not mean that you should restrict yourself to a small number of words, however. The language you use in your presentation, however simple and straightforward, still reflects your scholastic standing. It is a good idea to improve your vocabulary, since the broader it is, the better able you will be to think, to express yourself, and to understand others.

Test the extent of your vocabulary the next time you discuss a vital subject with a friend. Scrutinize your speech to make sure that he will not misunderstand any of your thoughts. Once you look at your speech, trying to eliminate ambiguity, you quickly realize that each word has a specific quality and function which makes it so unique that it fits into your thought pattern very accurately. If you find this method of self-analysis difficult to practice while concentrating on what is being said, review some of your recent writing in the same light. Look at it as though you were on trial and the lawyer for the other side were trying to pick on your words and twist their meaning. Incidentally, if you should write your speech as part of your practice, this is an excellent way of checking on clarity and proper vocabulary beforehand. You can also use a recording or dictating device when you practice your speech to obtain the same effect.

One final test for your own vocabulary control involves the use of a list of synonyms. Take some of the simpler words with which you are very familiar and go through a list of synonyms in a good dictionary. Try to explain to yourself the real difference between the various words on the list. This can easily be done by making up similar sentences on the same general subject, bringing out the difference between the words. Score yourself honestly and start working on your vocabulary improvement now.

Increasing your vocabulary

It is interesting to note how unfamiliar we are with our own English vocabulary. For instance, Webster's New Collegiate Dictionary, an average dictionary, has 125,000 entries in its sixth edition. However, Professor Terman of Stanford University published a study several years ago in which he claimed that the average fourteen-year-old child knows about 9,000 words, the average adult about 11,700, and a superior adult about 13,500 words. In the same study, Professor Terman estimated that the words actively used by the average adult in daily conversation number about 2,000. This is a far cry from the number of entries in the average dictionary.

It is also interesting to note that when studies were made of the frequency with which words appear, the two words "and" and "the" account for nearly ten percent of the written or spoken words. Seven additional words, of, I, a, in, that, to, you, make up another fifteen percent of the spoken and written words. Professor Terman provides a list of fifty words (including the nine cited above) which actually comprise fifty percent or more of our everyday vocabulary. He also notes that only one of these fifty words is multisyllabic. He concludes his observations with the fact that one thousand words account for ninety-one percent of our commonly used language, which means that we experience only a slight degree of individual adaptation of English to our speech needs.

To convince yourself of the statistics above, select a page at random from any standard dictionary. Now, on both sides of the page, carefully check the number of words with which you are thoroughly familiar, and the number of those which may be included only in your "recognition" or inactive vocabulary. Compare the number of words with which you are at all familiar with the number of words on the same two pages that are unknown to you. This ratio should then be applied to the total number of words in the dictionary to determine how many of these words are in your vocabulary. Also, estimate the number of words in the dictionary which you are thoroughly familiar with and which make up your inactive vocabulary. (Be sure that the particular pages selected do not include technical words either in your own field, which would influence your calculation in your favor, or in an unknown field, which would give you an unusually low mark.)

A more accurate method of calculating your vocabulary would involve a similar analysis of two pages for each letter in the alphabet; this would give you a total of fifty-two pages to analyze. Now find the average number of words that you are familiar with per page. This should then be multiplied by the total number of actual pages of words in the dictionary (that is, such sections as pronouncing gazetteers, lists of synonyms, names, etc., should be omitted in this calculation). This method will then provide you with a much more accurate estimate of the number of words in your personal vocabulary.

This short, statistical discussion points vividly in only one direction: to the fact that many words either in your dormant vocabulary or completely unknown to you, if mastered by you, will greatly increase your capacity for efficient communication.

There is no doubt, therefore, that you should strive to increase your vocabulary. There are many methods of vocabulary building, but above all, you should continually seek new words: when reading the daily paper, listening to the news, talking to your friends, or in your professional activities. In addition, you should constantly try to use these new words, since words are really acquired only when you work with them.

As you strengthen your vocabulary and become more conscious of words, you will find that each word has its own unique and specific characters. You must seek them out in order to be able to lend your speech more forcefulness. When you pursue this method of vocabulary analysis, you can often be surprised at the indifferent attitude that most people take to the correct usage of their tools of speech. There is no excuse for the sloppy use of language.

Many books and other devices useful for vocabulary building are available. They are written mostly with nonscientific and nonengineering applications in mind. However, it should be relatively simple to adapt these to your own purposes. Ignore those sections which are strictly oriented toward poetic or other artistic needs. One valuable set in the author's library is Roget's International Thesaurus in Volume I, and the Vocabulary Builder by Smith and Greenhouse in Volume II. Several dictionaries, including technical and scientific ones, augment this supply of useful reference works. The author has also found the lists of synonyms and antonyms in most dictionaries helpful. But, for new terms or ways of expressing a scientific or technical message, the thesaurus has proved to be particularly valuable because of its cross linkage of ideas and words throughout. For those who are not familiar with the thesaurus, it is highly recommended as a standard reference book for the speechmaker and the technical writer. Fowler's *Dictionary for Modern English Usage* is an excellent guide for the proper use of each word.

Other methods of vocabulary building include crossword puzzles, the hunt for word origins, word games, etc. One method frequently used by the author doubles also for note-taking during lectures and technical presentations. With a pad in hand, you can follow the speaker through his subject, making occasional notes on highlights of his presentation. These can be reviewed and expanded later at your leisure. (Incidentally, the copious note-taking practiced by many students should be avoided by the adult scientist or engineer. This prevents you from absorbing the message of the speech and is usually unnecessary, since printed reports are generally available.) However, while taking these notes of highlights, it is easy to include the words that are unfamiliar to you or those that are used in a new way. This practice has enabled the author to learn many terms which were previously unfamiliar to him.

SUMMARY

The accurate use of words is the secret of success in speechmaking, especially when the message is delivered with enthusiasm and neither the audience nor the speaker is conscious of the individual words in the speech. The author does not recommend that the speaker use a complicated, multisyllabic vocabulary which is intended to impress the audience rather than to convey an idea. The author recommends the use of a well-selected variety of everyday words to convey the message precisely. In order to use this type of vocabulary without continuously repeating the same terms, it is necessary to consciously work on increasing your vocabulary in everyday life.

The use of slang, poor phraseology, bad grammar, and other incorrect usage in everyday speech must be avoided. This soon results in an improvement in the choice of words and benefits the speaker in every facet of communication.

The use of dictionaries, the thesaurus, and other vocabulary-building aids is a must when preparing a speech. The main point to remember is that the sentence is built around an idea and the words are merely tools. Never build your sentences about impressive phrases; you may thus destroy your message and lose your audience.

5   *Some Tools with Which To Make Your Point*

INTRODUCTION

There is no substitute for sincerity and simplicity of expression in the presentation. There are several methods with which you can amplify and emphasize your message. The schooled public speaker and some others have the natural capability of using those tools with little knowledge or effort. If you are not aware of these aids, it is recommended that you study the following paragraphs carefully before you prepare your speech. Then find the particular tool that will help you in polishing and rounding out your presentation. You should select it only after you have decided on your message; the tool you have picked will then help you to organize your speech. Remember, your message and enthusiasm are still the most important part of your presentation. Speech tools are simply "varnish" to help in driving your point home.

The logical approach

If your subject is relatively complicated and you are not sure that your audience can follow your talk without many explanations and qualifications on your part, it is best to adopt the logical approach. It entails presenting a simplified version of the theory first, and only then giving the substance of your presentation. This always avoids confusion as you develop your subject. The author has found this approach of particular importance when using a standard theoretical foundation from a different discipline with which the audience is not familiar.

In this approach, you go from the "light" to the "heavy." First, you generalize to explain the background, theory, terms, etc. Then you work in the details of the talk. This prepares an audience unfamiliar with your subject for a complicated discussion. Remember that without such preparation, they would not be in a position to understand your talk.

To illustrate this point, let us take the following example. A physician is invited to give a talk on safety in a chemical plant. His audience consists entirely of nonmedical people. If he should elect to plunge directly into the various aspects of the chemicals in question, he would have to qualify each medical statement. In order to simplify his explanation he could use the logical approach. He would start with a short explanation of the ways in which poisons affect the human body. He would explain poisoning by inhalation, ingestion, skin contact, etc. This would be followed by an explanation of the degrees to which chemicals react with the body, and the effect on the systems involved. Once this oversimplified, general description is given, the doctor can simply and clearly cover the specific chemicals in question. This technique will eliminate some confusion and make the talk much more interesting to those who have no background in medicine. He has a good chance of getting the safety information across to his audience.

The logical approach is used in many scientific and engineering papers along with a historical review of the development of the subject. This is not only a good way of giving credit to others but also of demonstrating your own unique approach to the problem. It need not be offensive and, with some care, may sound entirely impersonal.

Remember that the most important aspect of this approach is the general background information that is provided. You are making sure that the presentation is not above the level of knowledge of any member of the audience. In addition, many people do not admit to themselves that their school knowledge has become quite obsolete and is sometimes simply forgotten. Therefore, a careful historical review of events is most welcome. It might appear to you at first glance that preparing the ground in this way will be insulting to the audience. You obviously must carefully consider the type of audience that you have and decide whether or not this attitude is appropriate and inoffensive. In general, you will find the method applicable and most rewarding.

This technique of going from the light, introductory material into the heavier presentation is also helpful in other respects. A well-qualified individual may make statements based on his thorough knowledge of the field. These might appear controversial to the listeners because they have inadequate training in the subject. If you know beforehand that your subject is controversial and your attitude unusual, consider the use of this excellent method. You will not be misquoted or taken out of context if you prepare the ground for the body of your presentation.

One final remark: you have been selected and invited by an organization to talk to its membership. This implies that you have been selected as an authority. You have been given the assignment to teach the audience as much as you can about the subject at hand. In this respect, your personal preparation of the material and your intimate knowledge of the field (as evidenced by your acceptance of the task) entitle you to select any method of presentation you desire. This definitely includes the "logical approach." The author can clearly state from personal experience that it is a very rewarding method. It usually results in close rapport between the audience and the author. It is mandatory, however, that this method be used without an overbearing attitude on the part of the speaker.

The comparison

If your subject, message, or attitude is a radical one, you may want to use a comparison in order to emphasize your point. This is a very effective tool in the hands of a speaker. The comparison is taken from everyday life. It is a way of bringing home your message in no uncertain terms. An example often used by the author refers to the folly of poor material selection and insufficient quality control of incoming supplies by a company. This is compared to a housewife purchasing light bulbs in a supermarket. It is obvious that the housewife would not knowingly purchase bulbs which do not work, even though they are wrapped in a fancy package. Furthermore, if she knew that there was a chance of their being defective, she would certainly check them if at all possible. This example can be expanded to demonstrate value analysis. The false economy in purchasing a light bulb which is slightly cheaper but which has a known, short life expectancy over one which might cost several cents more but has a guaranteed long life several magnitudes larger than the first is obvious. The final point of this comparison implies that the housewife does not really care how the bulb is manufactured, what materials are used, or by what process it is assembled. All she cares about is the performance of the bulb. This is analogous to the case of the engineer who is purchasing supplies for an overall assembly. He does not have to specify the details of manufacturing as long as the products meet the requirements or the purchasing specification.

Such a comparison is certainly an over-simplified case. But it serves to stress a point from a field which had received little consideration by the audience. It shows the similarity to a situation that is part of everyday life.

One word of warning concerning the use of comparisons in speeches. The comparisons must be well thought out beforehand. Make sure that they do not backfire on you. Special care is needed if the floor later will open for a question-and-answer period. In many cases, a poor comparison is seized upon by some listeners and used in a distorted form. It is advisable, therefore, to consider the possible misinterpretations of the example before using it to demonstrate your point. To return to the example cited above, the author in this case was faced with such a "distorted" question. It concerned the easy breakage of light bulbs and how the quality of the product of which they were being compared would be affected. In this particular case, the subject under discussion was a solid metallic object, not easily broken, and thus the question was meaningless. Fortunately, the question was taken by the audience as a joke, and the author was not even required to comment on it. However, this serves to point out the strange attitude of some people, who seem to want to assume the role of a joker in order to trip up the speaker.

The demonstration

As its name implies, this speech tool utilizes a physical "working model" or other similar device to aid in delivering the message. Unfortunately, not every subject lends itself to such a demonstration. However, the use of demonstrations whenever they are feasible is highly recommended. They greatly enhance the effectiveness of the presentation and especially add clarity. This speech tool is particularly suitable for the explanation of testing methods, complicated mechanisms, new designs, tools, etc. The use of artificially made, enlarged models which help to demonstrate the principles is, by far, the best way of conveying the concept.

It is difficult to explain the working of a piece of equipment if the listener is not familiar with it. Of course, visual aids in the form of diagrams and actual photographs are useful. However, a working model not only helps to simplify the presentation, but it also makes it easier for the speaker to bring across his point.

As an example, we can cite the problems involved in explaining the stacking of atoms in the lattice of metals or chemicals. Here, the simplest expedient is to use ping-pong balls, preferably of various colors, to show the atom arrangement. This is always more attractive than any sketches or verbal description. It has been used for years in the teaching of metallurgy and organic chemistry.

When you use a model or other items for demonstration purposes, you must take the same precautions as outlined in Chap. 7. The models or parts being demonstrated must be large enough so that they can be seen by the people sitting farthest away in the audience. The author recently attended a meeting where the parts under discussion were too small to be seen by all of the audience and apparently no large model was available. The speaker, however, very cleverly solved the problem by handing a sample to each member of the audience.

One common practice, which the author does not recommend, is to pass several exhibits through the audience. The reason this is not recommended is very simple; it detracts the audience's attention from the presentation itself. Only the individuals who see the items first obtain the real benefits from the visual examination. However, as these samples are passed from hand to hand through the audience, the time span between the discussion and the examination becomes too great for the exhibit to be meaningful. In addition, as the individual examines the parts, his attention is taken from the lecture and he is liable to miss some of the fine points. Finally, it has been the experience of many speakers that samples tend to circulate only part way through the audience during the presentation. Therefore, many people cannot see them at all. In some cases, they are preoccupied with the samples even when the next speech is presented. It is therefore much wiser to have a display with the same samples on a relatively large board. They can be displayed in the hall outside the meeting and viewed before or after the speech, or during intermissions. This way, they will not compete with the speaker in winning the audience's attention.

Another solution to this problem is a group of photographs handed out to each member of the audience. These could show a small group of objects not suitable for actual demonstration. Preprints can also contain the pictures and, if distributed beforehand, can be used instead of a demonstration.

The negative approach

When your talk is arranged as an "intensive pitch" to sell your point, it is often effective to use the approach of "you cannot afford to miss doing such-and-such." This technique, however, requires a large amount of self-assurance and a good deal of experience in public speaking.

Another facet of this negative approach is the use of the "wrong" as a contrast to the "right." Here is an example of the negative approach: "If you wish to break every light bulb before you ship it, you can find some efficient, inexpensive methods other than poor packaging techniques." Here, obviously, we want to advocate good packaging techniques and the point can thus be dramatically demonstrated.

To bring home your point with the aid of this technique, it is not sufficient to spout off a series of high-powered, negative statements, but the whole slant of your talk has to be geared this way. It is not always easy to adapt a technical presentation to this approach unless you do have a suitable message. This tool, more than the logical, comparison, and demonstration methods described previously, helps to emphasize a desirable solution to a problem. Further on in this chapter, we will discuss the "repetitive line" as one way of underscoring a point. The negative approach also requires a certain amount of repetition of statements. For example, let us say that there are ten steps in a process and that each one depends on the same basic philosophy of performing the task for better quality or economy. Using reverse statements, it is appropriate to drive your point home ten times as you discuss each one of them individually. In addition, you can describe the advantages once more in the introduction and summation, making it a very effective speech. No one can miss your message this way.

Whether your statements are positive and you make your point by a true negative approach or you use a contrary approach throughout to indicate the right way of doing something is entirely immaterial. The main theme must be repeated over and over again in a powerful way. This is the type of presentation that usually involves a lively manner of speaking and a lot of gesticulation; thus, in many ways, it is a theatrical performance.

To give such a talk, you must predetermine the mood that you should be in. It might be one of anger at those who dare to disbelieve or one of sincere enthusiasm in selling the point. Possibly the urgency of the message requires an attitude of pleading. Whatever the mood, it is essential for you to rehearse, possibly in front of a mirror and using a tape recorder. Predetermine whether you can effectively present your topic in this particular fashion. The author has had no difficulty in using this technique, provided that he *believed strongly* in the sentiments expressed. He prefers this technique to the less emotional presentations whenever there is a message that needs "hard sell."

The ridicule method

Another rather theatrical and dramatic way of emphasizing a point is the use of ridicule. When using this method, the speaker can take the attitude of, "If I didn't know better, I would believe that. . . ." In this effective method of presentation, rehearsal is important, and yet the delivery is normally simple.

By bringing out the exact opposite of what one believes or what is scientifically correct, it is very easy to establish the truth. The ridicule method can be very similar to the comparison method, inasmuch as it enables one to pick a ridiculous example and, through a series of well-thought-out situations, to indicate exactly what should be done about a problem.

To return to the example of the light bulbs, with the ridicule technique, you would elaborate on a story whereby a housewife would knowingly go to purchase a lot of light bulbs which do not light up. She would, in addition, try to pay more than is necessary for this item and possibly go out of her way to pick only those which are poorly packaged and perhaps even smashed.

Ridicule can also be successfully combined with the negative and comparison methods. Here, it would be possible to make the comparison so farfetched as to be ridiculous and, again, this helps to emphasize the points you want to make.

Humorous remarks

Although humor can be one of the more effective tools in a speech, since everybody likes a good joke, it is absolutely imperative to remind the reader that not everybody can tell a good joke. Humor in a speech, unless handled well, can be a real setback. There are no clear-cut rules for introducing humor into a technical paper. If you know that you can tell a joke well, then you should try the humorous approach. In long, serious presentations this helps to relieve the tension and relax the audience.

It is a common misconception that humor is a necessary part of the introduction or the beginning of a speech. Unless the speaker can blend humor truly and effectively into the presentation, it is much more appropriate to start the meeting on a serious note and inject the humor somewhat later on in the proceedings. The worst type of humor is a farfetched joke so remote from the subject at hand that several sentences of explanation are necessary to bring it into focus.

Let us analyze briefly how it is possible to work a joke into your talk. The observation has been made by most humorists that anyone can learn to be funny, but it requires hard work to accomplish a polished performance. This, above all, is the most important consideration for technical presentations. It is difficult to imagine that you can come up with a series of spontaneous jokes to fit a technical paper. It is recommended, therefore, that you plan your laughter ahead of time and use it as an effective speech tool to relieve tension and increase the attentiveness of the audience.

You should determine those areas of your speech which could benefit by a laugh. Jokes must be strategically planted throughout the talk. A good joke toward the end of the introduction or at the beginning of the body can serve as an effective means of establishing good rapport with the audience. Later on in the paper, jokes can serve as a relaxation point. Also, you can punctuate points that you have labored over with a joke. In this particular situation, a well-placed joke will help to underscore your message. Finally, some accomplished speakers find it beneficial to end on a humorous note. They leave the audience chuckling and find that it helps create the impression that their paper was well presented.

Above all, don't overdo it. The technical presentation was not meant to substitute for a comedian's performance. In this respect, Table 5-1 should be helpful in your planning. You are better off with too few than too many jokes, since you do not want to be considered a somewhat frivolous person who may not be a good engineer or scientist.

How to develop a joke and make it fit the paper

Much has been written on the subject of humor.[1] There are even several catalogs of jokes available to the public speaker.[2] It is relatively

[1] Recommended reference: Percy H. Whiting, "How to Speak and Write with Humor," McGraw-Hill Book Company, New York, 1959.
[2] "Treasury of Public Speaking."

TABLE 5-1 RECOMMENDED NUMBER OF JOKES

Introducing another speaker . . . . 1 joke maximum
Your own introduction . . . . 1 joke maximum
A short speech (up to 10 minutes). . . . . 1 joke maximum
Average after-dinner talk (15-20 minutes). . . . . 3-4 jokes
Short technical paper (20-30 minutes) . . . . 1-2 jokes
Longer presentations: 2 jokes + 1 every 20-30 minutes

easy to work humor into your paper with the aid of the condensed outline presented below. There are basically four categories of jokes which blend well into any scientific presentation.

1. *The Sudden Twist.* This is the type of joke in which the speaker embarks on a train of thought which is purely logical, with no indication that a joke is in the making. As the narration nears its end, the speaker comes up with a totally unexpected conclusion which constitutes a joke and, in most cases, is laugh-producing. A classic example of the unexpected end is the following introduction by Mark Twain.[3]

"I am here, ostensibly, to introduce to you the lecturer of the occasion, The Reverend Dr. Van Dyke of Princeton University; not to tell you who he is . . . you know that already. Not to praise his delicious books, they praise themselves better than any words of mine could do it for them. Then, is there any real use or advantage in my being here at all? Yes, I am here to talk and put in the time while Dr. Van Dyke reflects upon what he is going to say."

Mark Twain, who was a master of the subtle joke, starts out in a serious vein, apparently introducing the speaker of the evening, using extremely flattering phrases. However, his closing remarks are totally unexpected since they put the speaker, Dr. Van Dyke, in an unflattering light. This makes Mark Twain's opening a good, humorous introduction. This type of joke is probably the most common one and is sometimes referred to as the "vaudeville-type" joke. All that is required is narration which seems to be entirely appropriate for the occasion but which ends with an unexpected twist.

The punch line of the joke can sometimes be used over and over again if it has some direct bearing on the message. On several occasions it was necessary for the author to stress that established practices in technology

[3] From: Mark Twain's speeches.

are the result of the historical development of the industry, that they are now anachronistic, and that a fresh engineering or scientific approach is required. This is especially true in the field of soldering, which dates back to Egyptian times. This lends itself to the following type of joke.

"The art of soldering dates back to Egyptian times. Historians have found many unusual applications of this method of metal joining in ancient art and industry. Soldering was not a localized Egyptian art but many soldered artifacts have been found both in the Greek and Roman era, as well as in other ancient civilizations. Of course, the materials and techniques were extremely primitive. At that time, the sciences of metallurgy and chemistry were in their infancy. With today's knowledge, new materials, techniques, and equipment have been developed. These would have dazed the ancient soldering experts. The author has recently completed a personal survey of industry both here and abroad. To his surprise, he found that most modern installations make a concentrated effort to solder *exactly as the Egyptians did.*"

This, again, is a story which starts out apparently as a historical review and builds up to an analysis of a situation. The punch line, however, is not what is really expected, and therefore, the sudden twist helps to produce a chuckle but, in addition, it drives home part of the message.

Continuous reference to Egyptian art will slowly build up a certain lighthearted attitude throughout the lecture, which, at the same time, may still be rather meaningful.

2. *The Unexpected Exaggeration.* This technique relies mostly on a play of words where a phrase that has more than one meaning is exploited to produce the desired effect. For example: "Ladies and Gentlemen, in order to make your evening a pleasant one, I asked the home office to send us a very short speaker. They complied with our wishes and sent us a midget."

Of course, exaggeration can also be used as an effective tool of speech to drive home a point without necessarily being a joke. This has been covered earlier in the presentation. Remember that in the exaggerated joke, as well as in the previously discussed "Sudden Twist," the unexpected end, properly delivered, is the necessary ingredient for producing the laugh.

3. *The Nonsensical List.* One of the easiest jokes to produce in a technical presentation is that involving the nonsensical list. When you decide that it is time to inject some humor into a specific area of your speech, look for an area that lends itself to an enumeration of

requirements. The last item can be easily used to include a laugh-producing line. For example: "Let us summarize what is necessary to obtain a highly paid public speaking engagement. One must have an appropriate subject, some experience and reputation as a good orator, but above all, one has to be a relative of the organizer."

Here, the element of humor is injected by the unexpected ending of the list of qualifications. Lists and summaries are widely used throughout technical and scientific lectures. This is extremely attractive for a laugh-producing device toward the end of a presentation.

4. *Other Methods.* There are several other minor devices used by many humorists to obtain a laugh. These include straightforward insults, absurdities, understatements, etc. The next time you hear a good joke, one that you thoroughly enjoyed, analyze it. Try to determine what it was that made it funny. Because this type of joke appeals to you, you are probably best qualified to make jokes of the same nature.

How to tell a joke

There are several "do's" and "don'ts" connected with the telling of a funny story. If you have decided on your jokes, practice them well. Remember that you do not announce a joke; you start it on a serious vein and then you should pause, just slightly, before you deliver the punch line. This ending must be short and well rehearsed. Slight changes in the story itself do not, in most cases, change the effect of the punch line. However, make sure that you have the punch line thoroughly memorized since changes in it might embarrass you personally.

Some people feel that they have to keep a serious expression after telling a joke, especially since many television and stage comedians have mastered this technique. Many good comedians, as well as experienced public speakers, find it beneficial to smile and beam at the audience while they enjoy the laugh. It is therefore up to you whether you remain serious or laugh with the audience. This should come naturally. When to resume the technical presentation after a joke is something that has to be sensed on each occasion. It is really not necessary for the scientist or engineer to wait until the last laugh has died before resuming his lecture.

Don't be embarrassed if your joke does not go over. The same story, told to different audiences, might bring about different reactions. Basically, people like to be amused and want to enjoy a joke. However, when the material is relatively serious, people might not react with loud laughter. Nevertheless, they enjoy the joke and you may recognize some grins on their faces. This should not discourage you from continuing your presentation and introducing additional, preplanned jokes. If you are exasperated, however, you can always remark, "My wife told me I couldn't tell this joke," or any similar self-critical remark. This will ease the situation and might bring laughter the next time around.

To summarize, let's review the "do's" as follows.

1. Practice telling your joke well. Make sure that you have memorized the punch line.

2. Start out in a serious vein so that you can surprise your listeners with a punch line.

3. Pause slightly before the punch line to dramatize it and remember to pause after the punch line, too.

4. Keep the punch line short.

There are also things not to do, as follows.

1. Don't announce a joke; you will lose the element of surprise.

2. Don't read your story or punch line.

3. Don't explain the punch line or apologize for it.

4. Don't use obscene language, slang, or tell risqué stories; they don't fit into a technical presentation.

5. Don't get discouraged if you don't hear laughter; the audience may still have enjoyed your story.

The repetitive line

One additional speech tool which we have briefly touched upon in this chapter is the repetitive line. Try to condense the main portion of your message into one line. You will find properly spaced repetitions of your slogan beneficial in driving the message home.

Although it has been considered in poor taste to repeat the same phrases, sentences, and words in writing, repetition of certain slogans can be advantageous. It enables you to center all of your facts around this one central theme. This serves to emphasize the message and imprints it in the audience's memory.

This speech tool is especially useful when a new method is introduced, as in the case of new concepts which are to be implemented within an organization, or when an item is sold to the audience.

Most speakers who use this technique find that they do not want to change even one word in the repetitive line. It is also customary to use this repetitive line as the title of the presentation. It is therefore extremely important that the wording be carefully worked out beforehand. A general recommendation is to prepare the entire speech first. Use the title as the first version of the repetitive line. Only after the entire talk is completed and polished should you develop a final, refined repetitive line.

This tool is most certainly recommended only for those who have had some experience in public speaking. You should feel at ease in most situations. To be delivered well, the repetitive line demands a certain type of dramatic showmanship on the part of the speaker and certainly requires a lot of practice. It can obviously be used in conjunction with all of the other tools described earlier. It is really only a supplementary, rather than a major, tool in the preparation of a speech.

SUMMARY

There is certainly no need to distinguish between the speech tools described in this chapter. They are really meant to give you some ideas on how to liven up your presentation. When you prepare a new talk, glance through your headings and decide which is best suited for you. Then develop your paper around it. If you are invited to do a lot of public speaking, you might tire of repeating the same presentation over and over again. Then you will find that reworking the talk in a different style might help you gain new enthusiasm for repeated delivery. Remember that planning the style of your presentation ahead will add much glamor and life to it. You will thus rise above the efforts of the unprepared speakers.

6 *The Personal Introduction*

What the speaker and master of ceremonies should know

The art of properly introducing dignitaries, panel members, lecturers, and other participants in programs is poorly understood by most masters of ceremonies. Therefore, it is necessary to avoid the mistakes that they frequently make.

The worst offense of this kind is the introduction that takes the wind out of the speaker's sails. You must remember that it is not necessary for the master of ceremonies to present the speaker's paper for him. It is a mistake and is in poor taste to use the highlights of his speech in the introduction. This is always very agonizing to the speaker himself.

Another common mistake is to dwell on the speaker's life in the introduction. Don't concern yourself with the details of his background that are totally irrelevant to the paper and to his achievements. Also, it is in bad taste to embarrass him with too much praise, especially if he is not an experienced public speaker and may not be able to live up to the audience's expectations.

The well-prepared master of ceremones bears in mind that the audience wants to know who the speaker is and what qualifies him to speak on the subject. Therefore, it is both customary and advisable to mention some of his professional achievements which have a direct bearing on the subject. A word might be said also about his standing in the engineering or scientific community.

Next, you should restate the title and subtitle, expanding them slightly. Follow this by relating the talk to the overall program in a few well-chosen words on why the paper was selected for presentation.

A few thoughts on how to compose an introduction are offered in Table 6-1. It is not necessary to include all of them on any one occasion and, of course, it is possible to add others.

TABLE 6-1   OUTLINE FOR INTRODUCTION

1.[1] Greet assembly and acknowledge dignitaries. Introduce yourself and your place in the Society. (Good morning, Dean X, Professor Y, Ladies and Gentlemen, and guests of the Society. My name is . . . and I am the Technical Chairman for today's meeting.)

2. State the purpose of the meeting, its program, and a few words on how the papers blend into the program. (Our meeting today will focus on. . . . We have X qualified speakers today who will spend Y minutes each to discuss. . . . There will be a 5-minute question-and-answer period after each paper, and another 30 minutes at the end of the program for further discussion.) (Your Society felt that we should have this meeting because. . . .) (The papers today have a common goal. . . .)

3. Introduce your speaker and state professional and society affiliation. (Your first speaker today is. . . , Director of Research and Development for. . . Company, in (city). He is an active member of our Society who has contributed to the. . . Committee, etc.)

4. List educational and personal statistics briefly. (Mr. Speaker holds a Ph.D. in . . . from . . . University and did his undergraduate work at. . . . He was born in . . . and now resides with his family at. . . .)

5. State why the speaker is qualified to give a paper. (Mr. Speaker has been associated with his present company for X years and, in this capacity as . . . , has become acquainted with the subject of. . . . His previous work with the . . . Company also entitles him to speak authoritatively on his subject for today. In the professional world, Mr. Speaker is well known for his contribution as author of the book . . . , articles, lectures, etc. He has received the following honors. . . .)

6. Signal the speaker to come forward, and then lead the audience in applause. [And now, with his paper . . . (give full title, accurately), Ladies and Gentlemen, Mr. . . . .] Start the applause here.

Note: Should the speaker have a long walk to the podium, you can add, "Mr. Speaker says that he will be delighted to answer your questions after the talk, so please jot them down as he speaks." Add this before you start the applause.

7. Yield the platform. (Shake hands with Mr. Speaker and help him with the lapel microphone, if necessary, and then leave the stage immediately.)

[1] Appropriate for first introduction only.

Remember that you are striving in the introduction to send the speaker on the road to success. You wish to introduce him in much the same way that you would wish to be introduced yourself.

An introduction should never take more than ten percent of the total time allotted for any individual speech. It should be made as brief as possible without sacrificing quality.

Once the introduction is completed, it is appropriate for the master of ceremonies to lead the applause while waiting for the speaker to come up to the lectern. When he gets there, the master of ceremonies should shake his hand warmly and possibly help him with the lapel microphone if necessary, before walking away from the center of the stage. This adds a personal touch and makes the introduction a true welcome to the speaker.

Once you, as the master of ceremonies, have mastered the art of public speaking, you may feel qualified to expand upon this type of introduction. Through investigating the speaker's personality and/or his background, you may come up with some well-chosen personal remarks about him. You may use your own experience as a basis for injecting some additional information about the speaker. Should you wish to try something like this, it is suggested that you meet with him beforehand. Find out what "special" information he would like brought out in the introduction. Use a sentence starting with something like, "Before the meeting, I had a short chat with Mr. Speaker and he tells me that he has recently received a special honor, etc.," or "Mr. Speaker, who is a modest person, let it slip during personal conversation that he has just received. . . ."

One item which requires special talent is the use of humor. To inject humor into an introduction is quite an art. It should not be taken as a must but rather as an option. You must make sure that you know how to use humor in order to add to and not detract from the introduction. (For further information on humor, see Chap. 5.) Remember that a joke in the introduction must be appropriate to the occasion. Avoid a farfetched story which requires several sentences to explain why it was included.

Finally, let us remember that an introduction is a speech in itself and should receive the same careful planning and rehearsal that a presentation receives. In many cases, the man who makes the introduction is as important as the lecturers. Do not read an introduction, although you may write down some statistical information. Prepare it well enough so that you can give it freely and dramatically, since you, too, are on trial.

Accepting the Introduction. Few people have learned how to accept an introduction gracefully. Most of them reveal their nervousness on stage by plunging right into their papers. In order to gain confidence in this situation, several recommendations are made.

First, thank the man who made the introduction simply by saying, "Thank you, Mr. X," if you know him personally, call him by his first name. You should then proceed to thank him for the nice introduction he gave you. Now acknowledge your audience, the dignitaries, etc., and pause slightly. Follow this as slowly and as dramatically as you can with the title of your paper.

Only if you are an accomplished public speaker should you try to inject other comments when you accept the introduction (these may either be on the light side or in a more serious vein). You may refer, for example, to the timeliness of the meeting or to the other papers.

As was indicated in the section on humor in Chap. 5, it is possible to inject humor with some simple, well-rehearsed phrases. Some typical ones would be:

1. "Thank you, Mr. X, for the fine introduction." (Turn to the audience and dramatically say, "You read it exactly as I wrote it!")

2. "Thank you, Mr. X, for your introduction. However, I was hoping that you would forget my name and call somebody else."

3. "When you gave your introduction, I was hoping that you'd continue until all the time was up and I wouldn't have to come forward myself."

Whatever your acceptance of the introduction is going to be, it is highly recommended that you prepare it beforehand and rehearse it as carefully as you did your speech. It is also suggested that you acknowledge your introduction immediately upon taking over the lectern. There may be a certain amount of unrest in the audience (people entering the hall, or changing seats, etc.). In this case, it is suggested that you take time between accepting the introduction and starting your own paper. Make the silence dramatic enough by staring hard at the people who are causing the disturbance. Let things quiet down so that the audience can focus its attention on your speech. Never try to outshout the audience or request quiet from the lectern, since this is considered to be in poor taste. The author has found it appropriate on many occasions to welcome latecomers, inviting them to take their places openly. In some cases, you may even inject humor into the situation with statements such as:

1. "Will the newcomers please come forward. There are some seats up front and I assure them that they can snooze up here just as well as back there."

2. "There are some seats up front and past experience has proved that I don't spit far enough to reach those seats as I speak."

3. "Gentlemen, please don't be embarrassed in looking for some seats. There are several over here and we will give you a minute to settle down before we start the lecture."

A word about acknowledging dignitaries, if you wish to do so. You should be sure that you have their names correctly or else you may be better off not mentioning them at all. You should also be certain that you are not violating protocol in the sequence in which you announce them. It is sometimes better not to acknowledge them again if the man making the introduction has already done so. Should you wish to do it anyway, and if you are not familiar with the dignitaries, you can always start out by saying, "Honored Guests, Ladies and Gentlemen," etc., and proceed with your lecture.

Writing your own introduction

If you are called upon to write your own introduction, which may occur under many circumstances, it is suggested that you follow the outline indicated previously (Table 6-1). You might be embarrassed in citing some of the facts, but you are still the most logical individual to provide the material. To avoid personal embarrassment, you might focus the introduction on the importance of the society and its aims or possibly on the concerns of the company that you are associated with.

When you write your own introduction, try to eliminate all irrelevant information about yourself and emphasize the points noted earlier. The main thing is to indicate to the audience why you are qualified (possibly more so than anyone else) to give the paper. Of course, it is also important to give yourself some credit for professional achievement such as special honors and publications.

7 Visual Aids—To Hold Audience Interest

INTRODUCTION

The popular saying "a picture is worth a thousand words" is very meaningful in technical presentations, in which the subject matter is prone to be relatively dry. Also, such visual aids as pictures, charts, graphs, and outlines greatly help the audience digest the information being discussed. It is always easier to assimilate data when you can both see and hear it. The audience will be able to keep up with the subject without having to hang on every spoken word. This is extremely important in most factual treatments since one piece of information hinges on another. If one stage of the presentation is not fully understood, the rest could become meaningless.

In addition, visual aids make your role as the speaker much easier. They serve as a sequence reminder for yourself. They also complement your verbal presentation by supplying details that you might have omitted. The average speaker is much more relaxed when he uses slides, graphs, or photographs while he is physically delivering his talk. Through the proper use of these speech aids, it is possible to assure yourself of an orderly presentation of details which otherwise could become mixed up. This is especially true with long, involved, one-man lectures. Here memory alone cannot be relied upon for all the details which should be part of the program.

Just as a poor speech can distract rather than stimulate interest, poorly prepared visual material can be a handicap. If it is too small to read or recognize, it is useless. In addition, the use of visual aids sometimes requires a darkened room. The speaker then loses effective eye contact with his audience. The combined effect of unreadable slides and lack of contact with the audience will doom the lecture. On the other hand, well-prepared visual aids can be quite an asset. They stimulate audience interest, make it simpler to bring across complicated data, and enliven the technical material. They are essential to maintain audience interest for prolonged periods of time.

This chapter discusses some of the material that can be presented in this form, and how you can benefit by using it. Preparation of visual aids, choice of projection equipment, and other matters are dealt with.

When to use visual aids

Visual aids are an integral part of any well-prepared technical or scientific lecture. They should never be used, however, unless they really contribute to the clarity of the material. The visual aids must not be considered as an entity in themselves. They are intended to complement the presentation, to clarify it and to help increase audience interest. If they don't contribute in this way, they should not be used at all.

Table 7-1 lists several general categories of visual aids which have been found beneficial. If you have never prepared any, you will find the hints helpful. More details on the mechanics of slide preparation are given later on in this chapter.

TABLE 7-1

Type	Uses	Comments
Illustrations	Equipment and other objects, photographs	Very important; much better than verbal descriptions
Graphs	Line and bar graphs, flow sheets	Best way to present data
Tables	Showing figure comparisons	Use only if not too cluttered; do not present unnecessary data
Word outlines	Trend of thought highlights list of ideas	Very effective, keep words to a minimum
Sentences	Definitions, equations, rules, etc.	Use only if necessary; explain all terms verbally
Humor	Line drawings or photographs	Very effective if well prepared

Illustrations of specific items, equipment
and other objects, etc.

In technical discussions, the illustrations of equipment and other objects are extremely important. Even long, involved verbal descriptions cannot always convey an idea of their shape. Actual pictures of the subjects or, at least, line drawings of them simplify your task in this respect.

Good photographic techniques·are essential. A picture should not attempt to show too much or too little of the subject. It is often advantageous to insert an enlargment of one specific, interesting area on the side of the picture. An example of this type of double coverage is given in Fig. 7-1. Remember, the photograph should show a specific parameter, relative size, simplicity or complexity, ease of use, etc. Without such a theme, the picture is relatively useless.

At first glance it appears that color photography definitely offers an advantage. However, you must be warned that the average subject needs

Figure 7-1

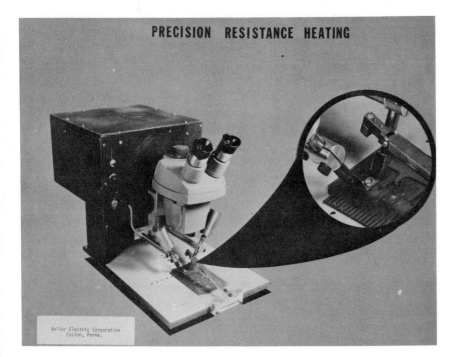

Figure 7-2   Example of Release Letter. (Note: two copies are required.)

Gentlemen:

I request permission to use the material specified below in a (book, article, lecture, etc.) entitled "_____" which I am preparing, and in future editions or revisions thereof, to be published by or presented to_____.
(Give details of items to be used such as: author, title, or exact excerpts to be reprinted.)

It is understood, of course, that full credit will be given to the source. The acknowledgement will be printed in the text or on the artwork where the material appears as follows: (1) As a footnote or credit line: "By permission from (name of author, title of book, publisher and place, copyright date)," or (2) as a parenthetical reference keyed to the bibliography where the citation will be given in full. (For printed matter only!)

Your prompt consideration of this request will be greatly appreciated. A release form is given below for your convenience. The duplicate is for your files.

Very truly yours,

- -

I (we) hereby grant permission for the use of the material requested above.

(signed) _____

_____   _____
(date)   (organization)

to be specially prepared for color photography. Without it you might get disappointing results, since the slightest irregularity (dirt, etc.) will show up in color. Fortunately, in black-and-white shots these details are not as apparent and thus not as disturbing. Such subjects as equipment in use, laboratories, and other large areas require a great deal of tidying up before photographs can be taken. In the case of color photography, they may even require repainting.

Line drawings of equipment and objects are often substituted for photographs, especially when there is some legal objection to using the photographs. Possible infringement of patents, copyrights, etc., may prevent you from showing a photograph, since special permission from the manufacturer or others may be required. This can be circumvented if the same idea is expressed in a rough sketch, universal in source and, therefore, nonproprietary.

The preparation of visual arts for public display is governed by the same laws as printing is. To protect yourself, you must be careful with copyrights and other proprietary information. If material is obtained from specific individuals, get their permission to make public use of it. They might require you to have a credit line appearing either on the material itself or in the text of the paper.

Figure 7-2 of this chapter shows a simplified letter for requesting material and permission to use the material for publication. This should serve as a guideline for this type of request. Remember that if you use photographs which include people, you must have their written permission before you can use them.

Figure 7-3

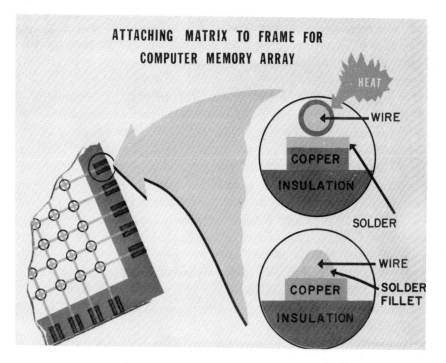

Figure 7-3 gives an example of a line drawing representing an application idea. The slide, incidentally, contains no credit line. As can be seen, the drawing is general enough that no credit line is required. If, for some reason, however, it is desired to protect the source of the visual material, the inclusion of such is a safe procedure.

In some situations, it is advantageous to have the same subject covered by both a photograph and a line drawing. This will help to explain some of the more intricate working parts or other details. The line drawing might consist of a simple schematic showing the operation of the equipment, or perhaps a diagram showing the circuitry involved. The use of schematics in purely theoretical presentations is also helpful. Simplified versions of hypotheses can often be illustrated in this form.

Simplify data presentation in the form of graphs, summaries, etc.

Statistical information, as well as scientific and other data, can be very dry. It is very difficult to sit in an audience and listen to a speaker quote figures and numbers. It is even more difficult to digest and draw comparisons and conclusions from such information. You must use visual aids or distribute printed material to keep in touch with the audience. Without these props you will not be able to transmit any valuable information. This group of visual aids falls into several general categories as follows:

The graph is a tool which is used throughout the scientific and engineering world. Any technical speaker should normally be used to this type of documentation. A clearly marked graph shows at a glance the high and low points of a series of factual data. This makes it extremely easy for the audience to follow the explanations of the speakers. Since more than one function can be represented on the same graph, the graph is also excellent for comparison of different sets of data. One graph grid with several graphs of relevant information is far superior to a tabular presentation. Data in tables is more difficult to follow and is not as meaningful. See Fig. 7-4.

Bar graphs are also an easy way of presenting statistical facts. The number of individual "graphs" that can be presented on each bar graph, however, is limited. Five is the least that should be included and you should never exceed eight for clarity of viewing. See Fig. 7-5.

The picture graph uses actual figures or line drawings to simulate the objects presented. This limits the items to be shown and, therefore, is less versatile. Use of picture graphs is strictly a question of personal taste. Some people believe that they help to increase audience interest.

The choice of the right graphical presentation for data is really left to you. Use the one that appeals most to you and that is easiest to prepare.

Figure 7-4   Composite Graph for Maximum Visual Clarity

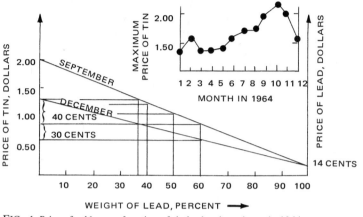

FIG. 1. Price of solder as a function of tin-lead ratio and cost in 1964.

Taken from "Printed Circuit Handbook." Edited by C. Coombs,
McGraw-Hill Book Company, 1967.

Figure 7-5   Typical Bar Graph

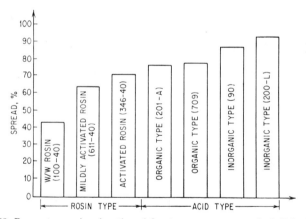

FIG. 3-43. Per cent spread as function of flux type; average spread of Alpha Metals alloy 111 on copper. The numbers in parentheses indicate specific Alpha flux used. Prepared on spread-rate analyzer under identical conditions.

Taken from "Solders and Soldering," H. Manko, McGraw-Hill Book Company, 1964

Holding the audience's interest with word-outline slides

Sometimes a speaker is called upon to deliver a lengthy presentation in the form of a seminar or a discussion. When it is a technical subject, it is apt to be relatively dry. It is the author's experience that the use of visual aids is an excellent method of holding audience interest for extended periods of time. The lecturer actually presents the written material and the slides clarify the more difficult facts or give a summary of the points made. If you arrange the visual aids in the proper sequence beforehand, it will be easy for you to pursue your line of thought in a predetermined fashion. There will be no danger of wandering off the subject or skipping any of the details. Remember, reading material from prepared notes is not desirable. It causes a great deal of distraction and the effectiveness of the presentation is quickly lost. Visual aids interwoven in a lecture is as close as we can come to actual textbook teaching during a meeting.

Updating of scientists' and engineers' knowledge by means of continued education on the college level is becoming more and more widespread. The author, for example, has established several annual seminars at universities. Several 17-hour-long lectures are given in two days which are designed to update the participants' knowledge of the technology of soldering and microbonding. To hold the audience's interest for such an extended period of time without visual aids would be impossible. To cover the tremendous amount of material without word slides would be an insurmountable task. The author, therefore, has prepared for himself a sequence of some 500 slides. These are used as a thread throughout the whole seminar which serves to maintain the continuity and establish good rapport between the audience and the speaker.

Word-outline slides are best prepared by using short phrases or title lists representing a sequence of ideas. This type of slide layout is discussed later in this chapter (p. 67). One very effective and inexpensive method of preparing these slides is worth mentioning here. It is common practice to present word slides in black letters on a white background for maximum clarity. The author has found the reverse, however, to be more effective. White letters on a black background are much clearer. One merely uses the negative rather than a diapositive for the slide. Adding color is also easy. Special liquid colors are available which will not ruin the film (do not apply them to the emulsion side, however). The title can even be made a different color from the rest of the material. If necessary, each line can be colored differently. These colored word-slides with black background give a dramatic effect. See Fig. 7-6 for details.

Figure 7-6

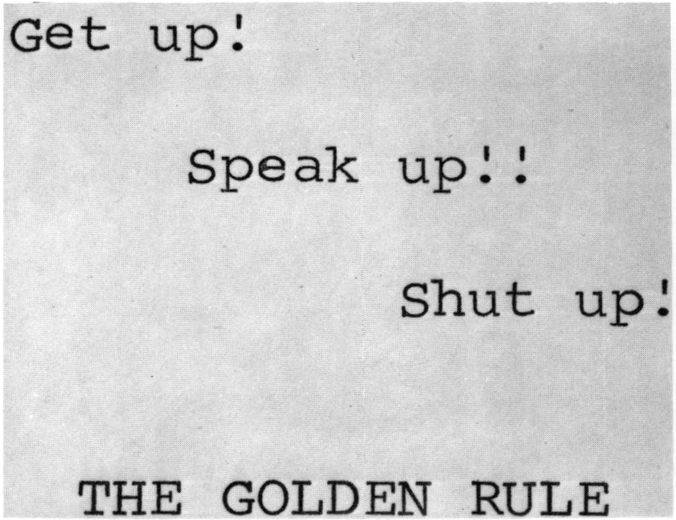

Get up!

Speak up!:

Shut up!

THE GOLDEN RULE

A

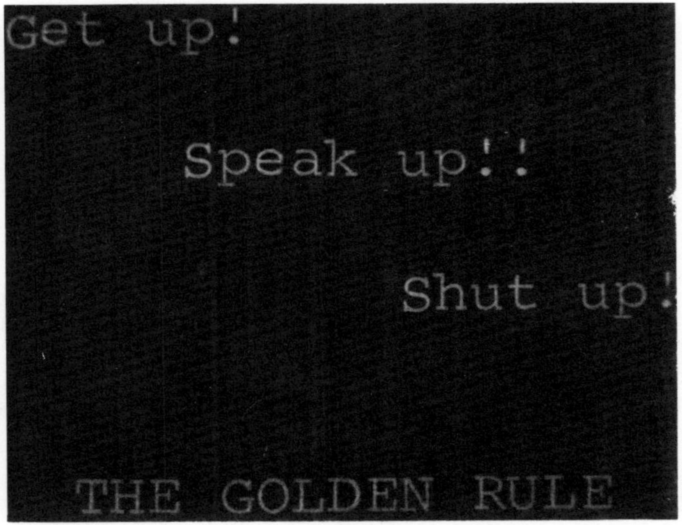

Get up!

Speak up!:

Shut up!

THE GOLDEN RULE

B

Note clarity of B which stands out better on slides than A. Also, simple application of color dye to negative (two tone; one for heading, second for material) will make this an effective color slide.

59

Livening up a presentation with humorous slides

Slides can also be used to inject humor into the subject. This technique is very advantageous, especially in relatively long sessions in which there is only one speaker. This is also useful with a succession of panelists where toward the end, a touch of humor might be appropriate. The humorous slide can range anywhere from the ridiculous to the exaggerated, with excellent results. You might have to use professional artists if you cannot undertake the task of preparing such material yourself. As an example, the author has shown here a typical imaginary device which our present state of technology has not yet enabled us to design. The slide simplifies the ideal situation in the form of the Joint-Sniffler. See Fig. 7-7.

Figure 7-7

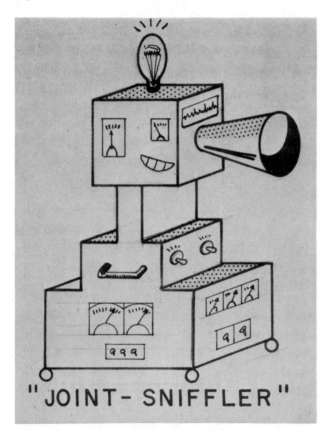

This device would make the inspection of electrical connections an easy matter and, therefore, would be highly desirable. However, as ridiculous as such a device might sound, it points out the necessity for a certain trend of thought. This slide is always used with great success to perk up the audience and to interest them in the material to follow, which, essentially, is a dry technical discussion of the necessities of inspection and quality control.

Types of projection equipment

The following brief discussion of projection equipment is meant mainly for those who have not yet selected a specific system. We will try to indicate in each case the pros and cons of the system. The relative price and ease of use, as well as the availability in meeting halls, businesses, etc., will be considered.

Let us treat these in their order of popularity but not necessarily in the order of their quality or price (see Table 7-2). The most common piece of projection equipment is the slide projector, with regular wall charts, flip charts, etc., being almost as popular. Then come the overhead projector, the opaque projector, and, finally, the movie projector and closed-circuit television.

The Slide Projector. Slide projectors are the most popular means of presenting visual material in lectures, seminars, and other discussion groups. The average camera hobbyist may use slides instead of photographs for everyday subjects. They are much more economical than color photographs. He is able to project these at home on a screen with relatively inexpensive equipment. This is an extremely popular hobby, thus mass-production techniques have been applied to make the price of the equipment attractive. However, the slide projectors used by professionals are somewhat more sophisticated. Let us, therefore, start with the least expensive slides, called "paper mounts," and work our way to the expensive lantern slides.

Paper mounts come in two sizes: the regular 35 mm frame and the super size. Both of these are mounted in cardboard frames which have outside dimensions of 2 X 2 in. This particular type of slide is the least expensive but, at the same time, the most vulnerable to damage. First, the film is unprotected and, therefore, is liable to be marked by fingerprints, dirt, and scratches. Second, due to the intense heat of the projection bulb (which is relatively close to the slide), the film is apt to "pop." By this we mean that it buckles and changes its shape, going out of focus. Both black-and-white and color film have this "popping" problem. Finally, the slides tend to fade due to the heat; this is especially true of color films. Thus, prolonged showing of a single paper slide is not recommended. This type, however, is the type most commonly used by amateur photographers. This kind of slide fits into most of the projectors available on the market.

TABLE 7-2

Type	Audience	Equipment Availability	Remarks
Lantern slide (3¼ x 4 in.)	Any size	Good	Highly recommended
Super slides (2 x 2 in.)	Medium to small	Good, but make sure that appropriate tray is provided	Must be mounted in glass for prolonged showing*
35 mm slides (2 x 2 in.)	Medium to small		
Overhead projector	Medium to small	Good	
Opaque projector	Small	Poor	
Wall charts	Small	None	Hard to see
Movies	Any size	Good	
Closed-circuit TV	Small	Poor	

*Unless they are protected by glass, slides will buckle. Remember that glass-mounted slides require special trays or magazines in most projectors.

It is possible to protect the film from fingerprints, dust, and general aging and, at the same time, to provide it with a heat barrier that will eliminate buckling and fading. This is achieved by sandwiching the film between two glass plates. Such slides are called "glass mounted" slides. These have the same outside dimensions as the paper mounts. However, out of necessity, they are thicker and, therefore, are not accepted by many of the projectors used by amateur photographers. Before contemplating the use of these rugged glass-mounted slides, you must ascertain that the equipment to be used will accept these thicker mounts. In some cases, it is only necessary to use a special tray in the automatic slide projectors that are commonly available.

The buckling of the slides in paper mounts can cause quite a variety of problems. The slides will seem to go out of focus during a presentation. This is caused by the physical change in their dimensions and, therefore, also the location of the slide within the optical system of the projector. By confining them in glass, refocusing is not required. Several inexpensive types of projectors are manufactured with a "preheating" stage. Here the temperature of the slides is slowly increased while they are in the holding tray, before they ever reach the projection slot. It is hoped that they will expand and, therefore, not buckle during projection and "pop" out of focus. The author has found this type of projector to be completely unsatisfactory for long presentations, especially when the slide is projected on the screen for as long as five to seven minutes. The continual focusing and refocusing of the slides and their fading make the long-term maintenance of paper mounted slides extremely costly and difficult. Some modern projectors have a built-in focusing mechanism. These projectors are very good with glass slides and are not as bad with paper slides as some other projectors are.

The importance of slide-to-projector compatibility cannot be over-emphasized. Two important factors should be predetermined. First, will the projector take glass slides with metal or plastic frames? If so, will a special tray or magazine be required? For instance, the well-known Kodak Carousel projector takes glass-mounted slides. However, a special "Universal" tray is required. The standard Carousel tray is definitely not adequate. Second, each make of projector takes its own tray or magazine. You might wish to prearrange the slides in such a tray; therefore, be sure you know what type of projector will be used. Prearranging the slides helps to prevent incorrect sequences and also the accidental showing of a slide upside-down or backwards. In any event, the slides should always be numbered on the side facing the bulb, in the top right-hand corner. In case there is no slide projector available at the proposed meeting location, do not worry. This type of equipment is always easily rented from any photographic supply store in all major cities. The rental for such equipment is relatively inexpensive.

The Lantern Slide. In order to project slides on large screens for big audiences, professional, large-size, glass-mounted slides are available. These are called the "lantern slides" and their outside dimensions are 3¼ × 4 in. These larger slides make it possible to enlarge the image onto a big screen in a large auditorium without losing definition and clarity. Lantern slide projectors are relatively cumbersome and are thus not used in the average home. Auditoriums, or even hotels, that cater to various technical meetings, however, are always equipped with this type of projector. They are considered a must in presentations to audiences numbering over 150 people. Since slides are usually made from artwork, the author has found it advantageous to simultaneously make lantern and 35 mm slides. If you plan to reuse your slides, just make and keep duplicate files of them all. This will give you versatility and you can easily adjust to the size of your audience. The transportation of lantern slides requires large wooden boxes. Such a box with 100 slides will weigh roughly 20 pounds; this might be a disadvantage if a lot of flying is contemplated.

In general, glass slides are the most versatile means of visual aid presentation. They can be adapted to black-and-white or color and can present graphs, drawings, photographs, etc. Any material that can be put in front of a camera can be captured this way. Slides are also easy to store, file, classify, and reuse in different sequences. This will be discussed later on in a special section ("Reuse of Artwork," p. 70). The 2 X 2 in. (35 mm) slides are lighter, cheaper, and more commonly used. For large audiences, lantern slides are recommended.

Wall and Flip Charts. For smaller groups where original-size artwork and other visual aids can be presented, charts are probably the most inexpensive and easily prepared visual material. They can be quickly made by the average lecturer and, therefore, require no cumbersome photographic equipment, etc. Only on very formal occasions is an artist's service required. In the preparation of such material, the use of white paper and various colored pens or inks is recommended. This type of material, however, is usually a "one-time" affair. Its storage and reuse are difficult and a new set of charts is normally prepared for other occasions. You should never attempt to use this type of artwork for groups of over 30 people. The details of such charts will be difficult for large audiences to see.

Overhead Projectors. The overhead projector is a piece of equipment which enables the speaker to sit facing the audience while he presents the artwork. The equipment is suitable for use only with transparent projection material. This can either be prepared beforehand or can be sketched on the spot. Photographed material or grease-pencil drawings on transparent film are used. In this way, the overhead projector serves as a blackboard for the speaker. You can intermix prepared slides with material that you are sketching as you go along. This type of projector, however, requires something of an artistic inclination on your part and definitely requires getting used to. It is not recommended for the novice speaker who will have trouble enough concentrating on proper delivery. The availability of overhead projectors is also limited. Some auditoriums are equipped for these projectors, but the projectors are not readily obtainable.

The Opaque Projector. The opaque projector is another piece of equipment which is used in technical discussions. It is operated by the speaker as he faces the audience or by someone else located farther back in the room. The opaque projector contains an arrangement of lights and mirrors which makes it possible to project any material from books or flat sheets of paper in black-and-white or color. This piece of equipment requires no special artistic skill on the part of the speaker and, in that respect, resembles the slide projector more closely than the overhead projector. Here, again, heat is generated by the bulbs. An air draft is created to ventilate the equipment and stop the projector from overheating. This sometimes causes trouble with "popping" of pages. This, in turn, makes the material appear out of focus. Therefore, some units are provided with a special protective glass.

Opaque projectors offer the least expensive method of visual aid presentation. Textbooks can even be used in presentations which utilize opaque projectors, since no photography or other intermediate steps are required in this method. It is sufficient to prearrange the pages and figures that will be projected in the lecture.

Movies and Closed-circuit Television. Movies, and for that matter, closed-circuit television are probably the most realistic types of visual aids. But they eliminate the role of the speaker, since the sound and the animation of the presentations do not require an additional person. They require no more than an introduction and possibly a summation. They cannot really be included in our discussion as tools for the technical speaker. They should be used to supplement a long program by offering a change of pace. In addition, the preparation of movies with sound is far more expensive than the visual aids discussed earlier.

Preparing the artwork

Any type of visual aid basically requires the use of artwork in some form or other. Unless the material is intended for a single presentation only, it should be prepared in such a fashion that reuse is possible. It is important to remember that a presentation is never built around the artwork, but that the artwork is used only to supplement the speech. The author has found that it is best to prepare artwork only after the outline of the speech is completed. Then it is easy to see in what areas visual aids would be of real benefit.

Some speakers are not adept in the preparation of artwork and, therefore, require the services of an artist. It is extremely important to make the first version of the artwork as complete as possible. The artists are not familiar with the subject of the lecture. Such minor items as proper terminology, spelling, and the correct designation of units have to be prepared by you in detail. All of the drawings must be accurate. On the other hand, the artist is more familiar with the graphic arts. He understands the use of such things as letter sizes, background, thickness of lines, etc. He should be given the freedom to prepare the pictorial part of the slides from line detailed drawings supplied by the author without too many restrictions. It might be beneficial to make such drawings with colored pencils or crayons to emphasize the various areas. This can be then translated by the artist into shadings and other black-and-white, or even color, tones.

There are some general considerations which help to make the artwork uniform. Let us discuss in more detail some of the important elements of the average slide or artwork.

The Title. It is possible to make meaningful slides without titles. In most cases, however, it is desirable to include a title for each slide. The major objective, of course, is to allow an individual quickly viewing the slide to orient himself as to the exact meaning of what the speaker is covering. This, in most cases, adds rather than detracts from the value of the slides.

Titles are usually prepared in larger letters than the rest of the written material. They should consist of no more than four words, and preferably fewer. A title does not have to be grammatically correct. Titles should be placed in the same location on each slide—either at the top or at the bottom of the material. Most people feel that a title should be placed on the top of the slide so that the reader will look at it first. It is also possible to draw the reader's attention to the title by placing it on the bottom and making the correct differentiation in lettering size between the material and the title. The interchanging of the title in the material at top or bottom is a dangerous practice. It seems to clutter up the artwork and is therefore not recommended. Thus, even if the rest of the material in the slide is slightly reduced in size, the title should always be placed in the same well-defined location. You must instruct the artist on this.

The selection of the style of a title warrants careful consideration. When the artwork is first prepared, the possible reuse of the same slides in a different framework should be reckoned with. This requires standardization, or else there might be nonuniformity when additional slides are prepared at a later date. The author has found the checklist in Fig. 7-8 to be of great help. Let us discuss the instructions given in Fig. 7-8 for the title.

(*a*) indicates that titles should be centered at the top. This is by far the preferred style. From an aesthetic point of view it gives uniformity to slides, graphs, and photos or sketches. Some people prefer the title at the bottom but this is more difficult in the case of photographs and other pictorial material.

(*b*) restricts the number of words in the title to a maximum of four. This is dictated by the size and boldness of the letters. Also, the title becomes too cumbersome with length and loses its effectiveness. A long title requires reduced lettering size and thereby the title is less easily distinguished from the other written material. Here, headline style from newspapers, as well as abbreviations, are entirely acceptable. The title does not have to be grammatically correct.

(*c*) makes sure that the title is self-explanatory. The title is required to fulfill a certain function and unless it does so, it is useless. Most titles of slides are self-evident; all that is necessary in selecting a title is to ask yourself, "What do I want to bring out in this slide?" Sometimes this also helps in arranging the material on the slide in the correct sequence. Over-amplification in the title is definitely not required. It is always enlarged by the verbal discussion.

Finally, (*d*) gives instructions as to the type of lettering and the maximum size expressed as the total height of the slide itself. The author has found that 1/8 height is the preferred size. Titles should seldom exceed this size. Titles should definitely not be smaller than 1/12 size (all fractions are given in ratio to slide height).

The Correct Written Material. Here, again, let us follow the instructions given in (2) of Fig. 7-8. Basically, a slide with written material is designed to give a quick outline, or sometimes an enumeration of factors affecting the material described by the title.

(*a*) requires that the written material be aligned at the left. There is an artistic form that requires more space, in which the lines are slanted

Figure 7-8 Checklist for Artwork

1. Title
    a. Center at top
    b. Maximum: four words
    c. Is self-explanatory
    d. Heavier lettering (1/12 height preferred)
2. Written material
    a. Lined up at left
    b. Maximum: five words per heading
    c. In logical numbered sequence
    d. Maximum: six headings per slide
    e. Lettering no smaller than 1/30 height
3. Graphs
    a. Vertical unit identification preferred
    b. Use no grid, just calibration lines
    c. Maximum: five functions per graph
    d. Color or shade desired levels
4. Photos and sketches
    a. All must include title
    b. Superimpose material at top, right-hand corner only
    c. Credit line, bottom left (1/50 height)

Note: Number slides on back of artwork only. Check all spelling carefully to eliminate costly corrections.

diagonally across the slide. For the scientific presentation, aligning them at the left is the preferred style for clarity and size.

(*b*) specifies that a line should not have more than five words. Otherwise the lettering will become too small to be legible. Here again, as in the case of the title, abbreviations and headline style are entirely permissible.

(*c*) dictates that the material be presented in a logical sequence. Items should be numbered or lettered for ease of reference. They should be similar in grammatical style for uniformity (all verbs or adjectives, etc.).

(*d*) restricts the number of lines per slide. No more than six headings should be used in any one slide. The slide becomes cluttered otherwise, and the size of the writing has to be reduced in order to accommodate all of the material. It is sometimes possible to double up two items in one heading or, in some cases, to artificially divide a slide into two groupings and to present the material in two different slides.

(*e*) refers to the size of the lettering. In height, it should be no less than 1/30 the height of the slide and, in most cases, it should be larger. Here, the artist usually has simple rules of thumb to determine the size of the letters from the space available.

The Graph. We have already discussed graphs in some detail. Here are the standard instructions to the art department on their preparation. They follow the checklist in Fig. 7-8.

(*a*) concerns the identification of the units, which must be as legible as possible. It is preferable to have the identification of units for the vertical line in the vertical position. These are not as easy to read as horizontal lines but afford more space for larger letters.

(*b*) concerns itself with clarity. In addition, you should try to use as few grid lines as possible. Small, numbered stubs for calibration of the major lines are entirely sufficient. This reduces the number of lines on the slides; also, you may want to cite one or two values in critical areas, but no more.

(*c*) restricts the number of functions per graph. You should have no more than five functions [five well-defined lines which should be marked differently (i.e., dashes, dots, solid lines, color, etc.)] per display. If the functions seem to weave in and out of each other, the material might well have to be presented on several slides. Never clutter up one slide with too many graphs.

(*d*) refers to the use of color or shading to indicate certain levels, peaks, maximums, etc. It might also be extremely useful to differentiate between closely spaced functions. Once again, the use of colored pencils when preparing your rough drawings is recommended, but the final coloring or shading should be left to the artist.

Photos and Sketches. Both sketches and photos basically fulfill the same functions and can be interchanged and even intermixed. As summarized in the checklist, the instructions are as follows:

(*a*) All photos and sketches must have a title. This title should be located in the same place as it is in the slides.

(*b*) Whenever pictures are superimposed on a slide, it is important to insert them always at the top, right-hand corner of the slide. This, incidentally, is an excellent way of highlighting important, small areas which need additional focus; see Fig. 7-1.

(*c*) deals with the credit line. This should be placed on the bottom, left-hand side. Only in special circumstances should you deviate from this practice. The height of the average credit line lettering should be approximately 1/50 of the overall height of the slides. This does not detract from the material, and yet the credit is right there on the slide.

A word of caution is needed here to discourage you from using too many commercial items in your artwork. Neither your own nor another company's advertising should creep into the technical presentation. The fact that you are showing a picture and either skim quickly over the name of the manufacturer or even omit it entirely sometimes offers more persuasive advertising in any case. A long dissertation on the benefits of the equipment will certainly be interpreted by the audience as a sales pitch.

A Word About Color. A well-prepared color slide can add a lot of life to a technical presentation. The expense of making slides in color, however, is also a factor to be reckoned with. The conversion from black-and-white to color, once a certain number of slides have been prepared, is a difficult one. There is available on the market colored acetate which can be incorporated in slides to provide a color background. This can then be blended in with future color slides. However, the use of color is not really that essential.

As stated earlier, it is necessary to be careful with colored pictures of equipment. Color photography reveals details of poor housekeeping and other details which would be lost in a black-and-white picture. Finally, it is possible to intermix black-and-white photographs with color slides without any difficulty. This is, in many cases, a desirable combination. Obviously, such things as metallographic cross sections, x-ray pictures, or oscillograph traces are in black and white. You do not have to use color to give them a special effect.

Numbering, Storage, and Reuse of Artwork. In order to keep the artwork and especially the slides in an orderly fashion, it is necessary to arrange them in numerical sequence and to record them on a list. This will serve as a master file. Artwork should be numbered on the back side only so that it does not appear on the material itself. Slides, on the other hand, are marked on the frames. Here it is very helpful to always mark the slides in the same location, at the top right-hand side of the slide facing the bulb in the projector. The number will be visible and readable as the slide is inserted into the magazine or tray. This, incidentally, is the bottom, left-hand corner of the emulsion (dull) side of each slide.

Having all slides properly oriented is important. The emulsion side should face the projection lamp. If not, the writing appears from right to left in a mirror image. Upside-down slides can be very embarrassing. If these occur, face the situation squarely, and simply ask the projectionist to correct the slide position. If the equipment is automatic, keep talking from the slides with a remark such as: "In this upside-down slide we see. . . ." The author had the following experience, in which this occurrence was beneficial.

In one of my foreign lecture tours I was faced by a coldly polite, yet hostile audience of engineers and scientists. None of my standard jokes seemed to warm the atmosphere. After the usual opening remarks, I decided to ignore the frigid atmosphere and to proceed with the six-hour seminar. The projectionist, who was a personal friend, noticed the poor rapport and was rather overanxious. When I called for the slides, he overreacted and overturned the slide tray. When the hastily rearranged slides were finally projected, the fourth or fifth was upside-down. Because of the unfriendly atmosphere, I just said "oops" and continued without any apologies. To my surprise, this brought some smiles. The next upside-down slide seemed to break the ice and after several more, the audience warmed up. Although I don't recommend using this technique to warm up an audience, it might help bail you out of a tough spot.

It is suggested that the slides be given a numerical sequence which is identical to their first use. When additional slides are made, it is no longer necessary to renumber the old slides. Additional numbers are issued for them. A "lecture slide sequence" is then prepared for any new arrangement.

The slides should be stored in a convenient form and in numerical sequence. This is more difficult and expensive for artwork. For slides, there are many inexpensive, convenient storage boxes and drawers commercially available.

Lecture Cards—A Memory Jog. If a simple method is available for making miniature copies of the artwork, it is possible to prepare individual lecture cards as shown in Fig. 7-9. These are normally prepared on 5 X 8 in. index cards and the miniature picture or slide copy is glued to the top side of the card. The title and the subject highlights to be discussed are written or typed in. This card will make it easy to select the slides for a different sequence at a later date and the number which appears in the center of the card is the same number as is used for the slide.

In this way, a slide sequence can be established and the lecture cards can be assembled for rehearsal. They are also useful as a reminder during

Figure 7-9 A Typical Lecture Card

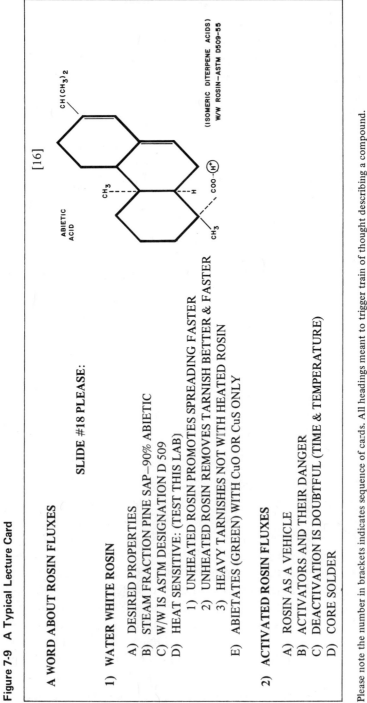

ABIETIC
ACID

CH(CH₃)₂

CH₃

CH₃

COO⁻(H⁺)

H

[16]

(ISOMERIC DITERPENE ACIDS)
W/W ROSIN—ASTM D509-55

A WORD ABOUT ROSIN FLUXES

SLIDE #18 PLEASE:

1) WATER WHITE ROSIN

  A) DESIRED PROPERTIES

  B) STEAM FRACTION PINE SAP–90% ABIETIC

  C) W/W IS ASTM DESIGNATION D 509

  D) HEAT SENSITIVE: (TEST THIS LAB)

      1) UNHEATED ROSIN PROMOTES SPREADING FASTER

      2) UNHEATED ROSIN REMOVES TARNISH BETTER & FASTER

      3) HEAVY TARNISHES NOT WITH HEATED ROSIN

  E) ABIETATES (GREEN) WITH CuO OR CuS ONLY

2) ACTIVATED ROSIN FLUXES

  A) ROSIN AS A VEHICLE

  B) ACTIVATORS AND THEIR DANGER

  C) DEACTIVATION IS DOUBTFUL (TIME & TEMPERATURE)

  D) CORE SOLDER

Please note the number in brackets indicates sequence of cards. All headings meant to trigger train of thought describing a compound.

the final presentation. The use of a lecture card with the miniature picture of the artwork enables you to stand in front of the audience without turning to the screen on which the picture is projected. You can concentrate on the material and whenever the slide is finished, can request the next one. In the meantime, you can prepare yourself for a few seconds for the new slide that will be appearing.

Once a lecture card is prepared, it is really ready for reuse in any other sequence. The card and slides will always bring back to the speaker the details of the material that he intends to present. Adding slides, rearranging their sequence, and the preparation of papers with a different emphasis are all much simpler than might appear at first glance. You are really encouraged to avoid repeating the same presentation over and over again. You will feel that, in most cases, you can improve greatly over previous efforts.

Maintenance and Transportation of Slides. Maintaining the artwork, especially slides, is also a simple task, especially when glass-mounted slides or lantern slides are used. Basically, cleanliness of any item to be projected is important. Fingerprints will be enlarged when projected on a screen and will cause not only blurred but sometimes even humorous effects. Various cleaning fluids are available for keeping glass and photographic lenses clean. It is important, however, to make sure that the solution will not affect the photographic emulsion used on slides. Otherwise, the material may swell and become fuzzy. Lint-free cloth or lens paper should be used at all times.

Transporting slides is simple. Many carrying cases are available on the market. It is important that you have a clearly marked sequence of slides with you just in case the slides should become mixed up. This type of lecture slide sequence should be printed on a separate sheet of paper pasted within the carrying case or in a notebook that you carry with you.

References. An excellent reference book on the mechanical preparation of visual material is the "Guide to Audio-Visual Presentations," which was prepared for the U.S. Air Force by the Battelle Memorial Institute and published by World Business Publications, Inc. This book gives a detailed discussion of how to prepare artwork, the various methods of projection and, in many cases, the details given are extremely useful, both for the mechanical work as well as the preparation of the artwork itself.

Another reference which, unfortunately, is out of print, is a booklet entitled, "Effective Projection Equipment and Copy Preparation Practices," An Author's Guide on Preferred Practices, prepared by L. S. Bonnell, C. R. Paul, Jr., and I. S. Rice, Jr.; printed by the American Chemical Society, September 6, 1953.

It is also possible to obtain many useful pamphlets from commercial sources such as the photographic film manufacturers. This information is extremely helpful if you plan to prepare the slides yourself. (See "Additional Reading Material," p. xiii, No. 5.)

8 *Speakers' Manners*

How to behave at the podium

If you have never given a paper before, you might feel inadequate. You don't know what to do with your hands and feet, how to dress, how to stand, and, in general, feel clumsy and exposed in front of your audience. This, however, is really only a matter of some thought and practice. These must be the feelings of an actor on stage for the first time and, therefore, could correctly be labeled stage fright. This chapter will give some simple rules which will serve as good starting points for the novice to develop a pattern of behavior. This behavior can and should be changed with experience, once you start developing a style of your own.

Dressing the part

To start out with, the proper dress for the location is probably the most important factor. It must make you feel at ease. Your clothes should blend in and once selected, should not be given any further consideration. Be sure that you are not overdressed but, by all means, be sure that your clothes fit well. Ladies usually have less trouble with this than men. Make sure that your jacket is properly buttoned and still permits a relatively large degree of freedom of movement. Should this be difficult, then you should consider buttoning your jacket until the introductions are over and you are beginning to give your paper. At this time, you can easily unbutton it and continue your presentation.

Remember, however, to button your jacket once more when the paper is completed.

Consider your clothing accessories as part of your preparation. Properly shined shoes, a well-knotted tie, and similar items should not need your attention once you are in the spotlight. Wear identification badges correctly; otherwise they give the speaker an air of negligence. And, above all, don't adjust or tug at your clothing while you speak.

Always find out beforehand the type of microphone to be used. Then make sure that no metallic objects are worn near the location where the microphone will be placed. If, for instance, a lapel microphone is used, no pens or similar hard objects should be worn in the breast pocket. In the case of a microphone suspended from a chain, no tie clip should be used at the same height. The rustling and banging of the microphone against these hard objects will distract the audience and confuse the speaker. The sound is amplified through the public address system.

Wear clothes that you are accustomed to. New clothes may be uncomfortable and require continual adjustments. Also, remember that in spite of the temperature that is normally maintained in a room, the speaker is usually hot. Because of tension, there is a tendency to perspire. The high-intensity spotlights often trained on the speaker don't help in this respect. Therefore, in order to avoid unpleasantness, don't overdress.

One last word about apparel. Sometimes in order to dramatize certain ideas, it is helpful to bring along certain props, and to wear them. The author is reminded of an extremely effective presentation given by a director of research. He was speaking to a group of salesmen about a new product. The man started his presentation bareheaded and after the introduction, with a well-calculated motion, he reached behind him and produced a college cap. He donned it and continued, saying: "Speaking scientifically. . . ." He then elaborated on the new scientific and engineering aspects of the product. Once this part of the presentation was completed, he removed the cap and donned a straw hat with a large sign saying "Sales Department" and said, "Now, as a salesman, here is what we can tell our customers. . . ." This type of liberty which a speaker can take will most certainly help bring his point across. In addition, just as the author has not forgotten this incident, the audience will remember the presentation in years to come because of the speaker's showmanship.

What to do with your hands and feet

The next subject to be discussed is one of composure and proper speaking techniques. If you are a newcomer to the art of public speaking and have not learned how to use your hands effectively in order to emphasize your message, it is well to keep them out of sight. It would help if a lectern were available since you could then keep your hands placed on the lectern, but by no means should you appear as though you were resting or leaning on the lectern. This is an attitude of nonchalance which can offend rather than impress the audience.

If hiding your hands behind the lectern is impossible, it is suggested that you study yourself in the mirror. Find out how best to hold your hands in order to appear both natural and composed. The author has often found that placing one's hands straight along the sides is the best posture for the untrained speaker. By no means should you put your hands in your pockets as this, too, is liable to offend your listeners.

Rocking back and forth on your feet, shuffling, kicking, or any other nervous habits are definitely distracting to the audience. This must be avoided and the best stance, of course, is that in which you rest on the balls of your feet, with your body inclined slightly forward; this gives you both ease of breathing for good voice projection and proper balance.

In some situations, it is customary for the speaker to sit in front of the audience, especially when particular types of projection equipment are used. Sitting behind a desk, or near a piece of projection equipment, requires no special instructions. It is considered poor practice, however, to seat yourself on the edge of a table in front of the audience (a pose which is often assumed, incidentally, by teachers and college professors).

After you have had some experience in public speaking, it is time to work on the proper use of hand gestures. It is absolutely necessary that these appear natural to the audience. Rehearsal in front of a mirror is the best practice you can have, especially if you can be highly critical of yourself. Such things as pounding a table or exaggerated movement can help to convey a point. However, this can only be used after all other techniques of public speaking have been mastered and you are at ease, without any stage fright.

From all of the foregoing, it might be concluded that the author recommends a stiff attitude at the lectern. This is far from being the truth. But nervous movements of a speaker will distract from his effectiveness. It is suggested that you start moderately and develop your hand motion techniques slowly. You should also refrain from nervous, unconscious but repetitious movements such as scratching your head, rubbing your nose, or pulling your ear. In many cases, this can become very irritating to the listeners. This is analogous to the continuous repetition of phrases or idiomatic sayings. When you have your rehearsal of the material, one critic should be invited to evaluate these points. These, incidentally, should not be taken as an affront to your personal capabilities, but as additional advice and items to be corrected to improve your stature. This individual should be asked to comment on your nervous movements and on any tendencies to be redundant. He should also be requested to count the number of stammering "ah's" which you use in a timed period of five minutes. A close member of the family rather than a co-worker might prove better for this "nontechnical review."

Never clutch or otherwise handle the microphone. This is a habit which many speakers seem to develop, possibly through watching comedians and artists on stage or television. It is considered taboo for a public speaker to physically handle a stationary microphone. There is certainly no need to handle a lapel or throat microphone, either. Remember that the professional microphones used in a studio are often concealed from the viewer through draperies or through the limited scope of the television screen. The one microphone which is apparently used and "manhandled" is not necessarily the only one and, therefore, could be of very low sensitivity. This microphone is usually supplemented by additional microphones placed above the head of the entertainer and at floor level. This is not the case with the public speaker, however. He relies on a single, extremely sensitive microphone to transfer his voice to the audience. Usually there is a poor arrangement of loud speakers, which requires a relatively high output volume. Any unnecessary friction on this microphone housing will cause unpleasant rasping. The speaker may not always detect these.

Eye contact—speak to everyone

The term "eye contact" is one that is little understood by many speakers. The value of the personal talk over that of a recording or a radio conversation lies in the fact that the speaker is physically present. You are naturally in a position to look at, and thereby to contact, each member of your audience. A gifted speaker who can maintain eye contact with his audience will unconsciously, but steadily, keep looking at one listener or another as though he were speaking to him directly. This not only helps to give the audience the personal feeling of closeness to the speaker, but also helps to keep the audience's concentration on the subject at hand. Eye contact is a technique which must be consciously developed. It is important to remind the beginner that there is a natural tendency to look only at the audience on the left and somewhat to neglect the audience on the right, with the audience in the center receiving most of the attention. You should continuously scan the audience, from left to right and back again, and from front to back and vice versa. Once you become aware of the tremendous potential of this means of communication, you can perform this subconsciously.

The author has employed an additional trick during long lecture periods. It is easy for a speaker to recognize a particular individual or group who seems restless or begins to show signs of boredom and possibly drowsiness. By talking to these people directly and with the appropriate voice modulations, the author has been able to regain full control. This calls for a very low and calm voice which rises suddenly to full volume. This makes the average individual startle and look up. By continuing to talk directly to him, it is possible to regain his attention.

In order to achieve good eye contact, it is not enough to continuously glance back and forth from one individual to another. It is necessary to maintain eye contact with an individual or a group for the duration of what would be a written paragraph. Thereby, the technique of eye contact can develop very rapidly into a continuous study of the audience reaction. This helps in the evaluation of the type of the people who are attending the meeting.

The author has also found that through eye contact, he has been able to gauge the level of audience interest. This very often has enabled him to expand and explore certain areas in more detail and to skim over others quickly. This becomes very useful after you become a good speaker and can vary your talk accordingly.

Eye contact, therefore, is a simple combination of a subconscious contact with the audience and a continuous feedback of their reaction. This also indicates the necessity for surveying the lighting arrangements before the meeting. Make sure that no blinding lights shine into your face. Nor should the audience be plunged into complete darkness, where no eye contact is possible. (See page 98 for further details.)

Eye contact is especially important when you are reading a paper. If you must read a paper for one reason or another, you should try to memorize it beforehand. If this is done adequately you will not appear to be reading it for the first time to your audience. You can then ad lib wherever necessary. Use a ruler or other marking device to keep your place continuously. Thus, you can maintain eye contact during your presentation by looking up every sentence or so and completing the paragraph while watching the audience. If this technique is not developed, you will have a very good chance of entirely losing your audience. You will also be inclined to drone and have poor voice modulation when reading. In general, therefore, you will not achieve the desired effect. The reading of your own speeches, in general, as indicated elsewhere in this book, is discouraged.

Voice modulation—don't drone

In spite of the fact that most people have good voice modulation in everyday speech, it seems inevitable that when someone embarks on a career of public speaking this natural gift is lost. There is in the beginning a tendency to use well-thought-out sentences with impressive vocabulary. This results in a definite droning type of tone with little voice modulation. With simple sentences, however, and the proper diction as defined in Chap. 4 of this book, the natural voice inflections auto- matically are restored. Furthermore, when a presentation has been rehearsed and the speaker is well versed in his material, there is no reason for droning. Every individual must show enthusiasm when he is giving a technical or scientific presentation, just as he shows enthusiasm in his everyday conversation with his family and friends. Lack of enthusiasm and the lack of preparation will always lead to a monotonous tone. You can overcome this easily by some simple preparatory steps. Don't try to create voice modulation artificially; it is easily noticed. The everyday methods of speaking which you acquire throughout your lifetime, with some additional preparation, are adequate. The ideal is to make your voice interesting enough to encourage the audience to listen to your message. This shifts the emphasis away from the words themselves that are being used. To achieve this, you must only develop enthusiasm for your message beforehand. Voice modulation will usually come auto- matically. When only a moderate amount of enthusiasm is possible, some rehearsing is required. Reading a message from a book or paper is more of a problem. The free choice of words and phrases is not yours. In addition, the written sentence is much more difficult to project than a spontaneous thought.

Voice modulation should not be confused with voice volume. Many years ago, in order to be a recognized singer, you had to have good voice projection, both for volume and effect. With the development of the microphone, the era of the crooners started. People with relatively shallow voices have made a definite place for themselves in the world of arts. The same applies to the nonprofessional speaker who is interested in presenting a scientific or technical paper. The volume of your voice can be easily adjusted through the use of the microphone. A high or low pitch can be somewhat adjusted through the use of the proper amplification system. If the quality of the speaker's voice and/or the size of the audience are not known in advance, it is a good idea to have an audio system even for small meetings. Many speakers' voices cannot stand the strain of continuous use, and possible voice failure can be averted by means of microphones. The author, for instance, can speak without any trouble for eight to nine hours per day with the aid of a microphone, even when he is hoarse. However, without a microphone, even before medium-sized audiences, speeches of more than an hour generally prove to be strenuous, even when he has a healthy throat.

Moving about the stage—the use of a lectern

When you are planning your speech, consider the duration of the performance. Any presentation of half an hour should require the use of a lectern, a podium, or at least a small table. This is the anchor point for you as the speaker. Try not to move from there unless visual aids require it. If the presentation exceeds half an hour and possibly exceeds even one hour, it is perfectly acceptable for the speaker to vary his position. But if you feel that this is hard for you, remaining behind the lectern is perfectly acceptable.

It is most useful to have a lectern or podium available on which to keep your lecture cards and other material. As indicated earlier, it is absolutely essential that for short presentations you do not lean on the lectern in a nonchalant way. Do not sit on the table with your feet dangling in front of the audience. In other words, do not show an attitude which will detract from the formality of the meeting.

In longer meetings and seminars, the environment changes. More informal behavior on the speaker's part, after the first half hour or so, will add to the warmth of the meeting. However, even with this freedom you must still refrain from such nervous mannerisms as rocking on your feet or playing with the pointer.

PART *2*

Organizing a Technical Meeting

Many technical societies are in a rut when it comes to organizing technical meetings. This problem is discussed in detail in Chap. 9. If you desire to change this trend in your society and to make a real contribution, you must help to reorient their thinking. Once you understand the real aims of a technical meeting, the rest will fall into place.

In addition to considering the program itself, you as organizer must also obtain the speakers. You must motivate them to follow the guidelines for a dynamic speech presented in Part 1 of this book. You must also take care of the physical details of the meeting. Chapter 10 is meant to help you with these tasks. It covers details such as the selection of the proper time and location for the meeting, setting up a hall, worrying about the lights, audio systems, etc. Chapter 11 outlines several stimulating types of programs and concerns itself with the details of the meeting itself. It offers hints of the master of ceremonies, and describes exciting forms of meetings such as workshops, seminars, and cracker-barrel sessions. The chapter ends with some straightforward recommendations and checklists to help you make sure that you have not forgotten any details.

With this information in mind, you should have little trouble whether you are the program chairman, a member of the program committee, or the master of ceremonies. It is hoped that this part of the book will help to give us more stimulating and timely technical meetings which aid in furthering our overall national growth.

9 *Conventions—For Fun or Learning*

**Updating the concept of the role of technical
papers and the professional society**

A technical or scientific meeting does not have to be dull. The
convention, technical society meeting, and seminar have become an
important part in the life of every engineer and scientist in the United
States. They help in keeping him abreast of the state of the art. The free
flow of the latest information as well as the personal exchange of data
and scientific techniques between the participants are as valuable as the
technical papers presented during these meetings. In many cases, the
meetings include a display of equipment and processes. These are usually
designed to serve in updating the audience's knowledge as to the latest
industrial developments. In addition, the exhibits serve the advertising
purposes of the manufacturer.

The convention—A place of learning or fun?

However, the picture, unfortunately, is not quite this simple. It seems
that the prestige of technical and scientific meetings has deteriorated
rapidly in the last several years. It appears that people consider them less
and less as places of learning; the general impression that such meetings
create is one of pleasure and fun. An analysis reveals that this has
occurred because of the poor quality of the individual presentations and
the negligence of the societies organizing the meetings. The trend could
be reversed if the individuals would prepare better lectures and the

societies and organizational groups would be more selective and judicious in their program preparation.

It is evident that the locations for technical conventions and scientific meetings are carefully chosen. The considerations given by the committees in charge apply only to the proper geographical locations, however. These are picked so as to attract a large number of people. Participants are even encouraged to use the opportunity to bring their families to these resorts. In many cases, these meeting committees take it upon themselves to arrange further tours to adjoining areas of interest and at group rates, thereby making the proposition even more attractive.

Unfortunately, only very little thought is given to the quality of the technical program itself. It is true that most societies screen papers submitted for presentation as to their originality and quality. But they very seldom set high standards for the physical delivery of the technical information.

In recent years, therefore, it has become apparent that most of the people who attend conventions take the opportunity to visit the exhibits and displays. They also participate in some of the subcommittee and committee work which goes on during such meetings.

The attendance at the lecture hall, however, is becoming progressively smaller. The reason for this is obvious. The average scientist and engineer does not know how to present an interesting paper. This is more of a problem than readily meets the eye. He seldom elaborates on the dry report which is published in the proceedings. The quality of the average scientific and engineering paper is not really at fault, however. The fault actually lies more with the appropriate selection of subjects (see "The Story of a Hoax," p. 88), which is really the function of the educational or program committee. In addition, untrained speakers must present papers in such a way that they will make an audience interested. They must also concentrate on offering the proper information, rather than on trying to impress the audience with their knowledge and stature.

This criticism, although it might seem harsh, is based on a series of observations by the author at several recent national conventions throughout the country. The level of audience interest and, therefore, of participation and capacity to absorb the content of the presentations is easily gauged by an observer. One merely has to notice the number of people who seem to be reading magazines, newspapers, watching decorations on the walls, or dozing off, in contrast to those who are actively following the speaker. The shifting around on the normally uncomfortable chairs, and the number of people who dodge in and out of the lecture halls in an obvious attempt to stay awake, are also excellent indications of the degree of audience interest.

When a well-prepared paper is included in a program, however, the audience seems transfixed. Close attention, barely any movement at all, no closed eyes, and complete absorption with the subject, are easily noted. It is this type of presentation that is desirable, and this book is intended to help to prepare them.

The written report and the oral presentation

The above helps to explain why the conventions have received reputations as places of fun and not places of learning. Much of this failure can be attributed to the poor delivery techniques of otherwise brilliant scientists and engineers. However, the role of the scientific societies cannot be minimized in this overall picture. Let us see how they contribute to the audience's lack of enthusiasm toward the papers presented. It is very true that a scientific society has to be very discriminating in its efforts to monitor the quality and format of papers presented at their meetings, especially that of those treatises which are to be printed in their transactions and will be available after the meetings to the general public. Therefore, the technical paper must conform to the same rigid rules which are usually enforced by universities and other institutions of learning. They must contain factual information and as much theory as is required for an understanding of the paper. This is the basic requirement of the conference transactions, which serve as background material for other investigations. Thus a paper intended for this specific use should follow the rigid format of Abstracts, Foreward, Summary, Procedure, Instrumentation, Results, Conclusion, Previous work, Literature, References, and Acknowledgments. But these are not the proper components of an oral presentation, since they would constitute a dull presentation for anyone but a researcher in exactly the same field. It is necessary, therefore, to really write a second paper intended for a wider circle of the scientific and engineering community. Here fewer specific details of the work itself are required and a more general view of the subject is desirable. Thus, it becomes apparent that not every scientific technical article in the transactions is really suitable for oral presentation. Many should not be included in the oral part of the program, although this might be considered at first as a reduction of the high scientific standards of the society. Close scrutiny will reveal, however, that this is necessary in order to regain the prestige which scientific meetings have had in the past.

The Story of a Hoax

In most technical and scientific societies, the members of the program committee are volunteers from throughout the industry and are not professionals. Unless there is some strong leadership or well-thought-out criteria governing the selection of papers for conventions, it is very possible that a paper submitted to a society will be judged not on its merit or suitability but on the author's reputation, the reputation of his company, or even possibly on the title alone.

In order to dramatize this point, a hoax was purposely perpetrated by a group of people. The story of this hoax is well worth quoting here.[1]

In this paper, the author presents a critique on the present status of technical papers and conferences in the engineering field and recommendations for improvement. It should be noted that his paper presents the opinions of an individual and in no way reflects those of any organization, commercial or professional, to which the author belongs. In deploring the low standards of good technical papers, the author states:

> The fault lies not only with the author; but with the people who run conferences and publish and review papers as well. To test this last statement, C. D. Simmons and myself decided to test the level of review of conferences. We arrived at this idea after having been thoroughly discouraged by the level of papers given at the 1962 International Solid State Conference given in Philadelphia in February. We submitted the following paper summary to the 1962 WESCON Meeting to be held in August of 1962:

> **"The Linotron-A practical device**
> **for Majority Logic**

> "The increasing usage of devices, such as the Parametron, has necessitated new types of logic to be considered. One of these is called 'majority logic.' It has extremely interesting properties when based on a best two-out-of-three or a best three-out-of-five decision mechanism. By itself, it can perform not only the majority function, but that of AND, OR, and EXCLUSIVE OR.

[1] This material is quoted, by permission, from a paper entitled "The Technical Paper Glut," by W. D. Rowe of the Sylvania Electronic Systems, Needham Heights, Mass. The paper was recommended by the AIEE (American Institute of Electrical Engineers), Technical Operations Department, Fall General Meeting, Chicago, Ill., September 17, 1962.

"A majority element is made up of two types of devices, linear input devices and a single active unit to assure that signal loss does not occur in transmission. The increasing importance and utilization of majority logic in logical design has necessitated the investigation and evaluation of highly linear devices and techniques.

"The Linotron is a practical solid state device for implementation of the linear functionalization of majority logic. This paper will report on several ways in which this device has been made in the laboratory, and to some extent used in circuits for various applications. A detailed theory of operation has been worked out and will be presented. This theoretical approach is backed up by considerable experimental evidence using various materials for its implementation.

"Fabrication has been made using Group IV elements, using both films and bulk methods. Initial results have been, to some extent, limited in accuracy; both high accuracy and very high linearity are theoretically possible.

"Operation of the circuit is based upon the motion of majority carriers which implies that the reliability of this device should be higher than that of most active circuits. Further, since majority carriers are the major mode of operation, the Linotron can be used without special packaging techniques or hermetic seals. The equivalent circuit for the device has been determined, and the description of operation will be discussed in light of these circuits. The equivalent circuit consists of passive devices connected in a series-parallel arrangement with a leakage generator.

"Experimental results have shown that in certain configurations the device is sensitive to temperature variations. It is felt that in some devices a linear relationship with the temperature can be obtained, making the Linotron useful as a thermal metering element. Some preliminary investigation in this area has led to consideration of a system with logical variations that are able to adapt to their environment in a manner to optimize operation. A change of environment essentially can be used to alter the logical operation of the system when the Linotron is used in majority systems.

"Various geometries have been fabricated in the laboratory. Several of these indicate that the process can be easily adapted to mass production techniques, and hopefully an extremely low cost logic element can result. Particular effort has been expended in the area of film techniques aimed at implementing these devices in a manner adaptable to microelectronics and integrated circuits. Configurations for low power dissipation have been investigated primarily although there is considerable evidence to indicate that devices with very large power dissipation are possible should applications arise. It is felt that this unique device will make the utilization of majority logic practical in large applications."

This paper was duly accepted for publication. However, we had proved a point and felt that it should be withdrawn. Our point was demonstrated in that our last paragraph would legitimately have to read as follows:

"*Acknowledgment*: We feel that the choice of a name for a device is an extremely important matter. We have devices called parametrons, cryotrons, magnetrons, and so forth. We have named this device the Linotron. We feel this is our most important contribution since we must acknowledge previous work done in the field. We must give reference and credit to G. S. Ohm, who in 1827 named this device a resistor.

"As is evident, this paper has described nothing else but a resistor, and it is basically a hoax perpetrated by the use of sophisticated terminology. This hoax was generated in all seriousness to demonstrate the serious deficiency in the content and review of technical papers in the United States. It is not aimed at WESCON, but all papers and conferences. WESCON was chosen only because of its timing and reputation for critical review. The fault lies not with WESCON, one of the better conferences, but with the whole glut of papers submitted to the infinitely growing number of conferences that make adequate critical review impossible.

"On the other hand, perhaps this paper glut is America's secret weapon. I've been told that the Russians translate everything we publish and circulate it throughout the Soviet Union. Perhaps we will exhaust their resources with large quantities of trivia. Further, with commercial procedures for paper clearance, which are most interested in patent protection, competitive position, and public relations instead of technical achievement, the papers the Russians are translating are probably one or two years behind the actual progress of work."

This story illustrates very vividly the importance of the proper selection of subjects to be submitted to the society, as well as the necessity for the society to set new standards in order to review papers and other material for presentation at technical meetings.

What is needed in an oral presentation

Our growth in all fields of science and engineering is so rapid that the old concept of the scientist who knew all has become ridiculous. Redefinition of the true meaning of a scientific meeting, therefore, is in order.

One of the most problematic areas in the lives of today's scientists and engineers is that of up-dating their knowledge through reading. In recent years it has become apparent that an individual can no longer read all of the material that is published in his general area of interest. Even if the material could be physically obtained, great effort would be required to read and digest it. The number of trade magazines, technical society publications, and other trade journals has steadily increased. In order to really keep up to date in his field, the average engineer must spend several hours daily in reading. It is also obvious that the average successful scientist does not have that much free time. It is this need for updating that the technical meeting can easily fulfill by proper selection of subjects. This is accomplished by gathering a group of experts in various fields and assigning them the preparation of material with this function in mind.

There is an additional problem caused by the fact that no scientist or engineer can afford to stop widening his horizons after he leaves school. With all of the material that is published in his own field, it is difficult for him to maintain an awareness of developments in other areas which might not be directly connected with but which could definitely influence his own work. Often papers in other than the society's specialty are of tremendous benefit to the membership.

A complete reorientation of the philosophy of the convention and its technical programs, therefore, could result in a shift of the overall attitude back to its previous serious note. By enlisting the help of specialists in every field to present the latest advances throughout the industry in a well-organized manner, it will be possible to make conventions more fruitful. Then the scientific and engineering community would again participate in a full day's lectures. These must be prepared so that they are of a high degree of interest, thought provoking, and stimulating. This would make the careful selection of convention locations in order to attract vacationers unnecessary in the future.

Guiding yourself for your next technical speech or meeting

With this idea in mind, it will be easy for you, the reader, to prepare yourself properly for the presentation of your next paper in such a manner that you will be able to avoid the complacency of today's lecturer and become a skilled speaker. This is not to underestimate the work that is necessary in technical or scientific speaking. Planning, writing, editing, and rehearsing are a must.

In this respect, it is interesting to note that some of the greatest orators of our times have followed the same rules. Winston Churchill, who certainly was one of the finest public speakers in the political life of our era, never made an impromptu speech. Most of his speeches were written out in full and then read; they were read beautifully and forcefully but they were, nevertheless, read. According to one of the secretaries associated with Churchill, the speeches were carefully planned in advance. First, a rough draft would be written, and then he would edit his own work, sometimes going over the same material as often as five times before he felt that it was ready to be delivered to the public. And if the man who gave us some of the most inspiring words during the darkest hours of World War II, such as "I have nothing to offer but blood, toil, tears, and sweat" (May 13, 1940), or the phrase the "Iron Curtain," would carefully and thoroughly prepare himself for his public appearances, the scientist and engineer most certainly must do so.

Thus, if you ever become involved in the preparation of technical meetings, keep the above in mind. The program should add to the printed proceedings. By no means should the speakers repeat what they have published. They must be willing to prepare a stimulating talk aimed at widening their listeners' horizons. Anyone in the audience who seeks further details should be referred to the transactions.

The next two chapters are designed to help you with the physical arrangements and organizational details of a meeting. With this information, you should be in a position to get a good show on the road, whether you are the program chairman or a member of the committee.

10 *Preparing an Auditorium for a Meeting*

If you have never been involved in preparing facilities for a technical meeting of any sort, you will be amazed at the number of details involved. In an attempt to minimize the confusion, the author will outline in this chapter the typical arrangements required for such a meeting. These will be summarized in the checklist in Fig. 10-3. You may wish to survey these before reading this chapter.

Selecting the right date and location

The proper timing of a meeting is crucial. Meetings that are set up either in conjunction with or in competition with, conventions usually do not get good attendance. Meetings should be scheduled so that they do not have any competition. It is advisable to avoid scheduling conflicts with any events which the professionals that you intend to have in your audience are likely to attend.

The second item to consider is the location. Public transportation and accessibility for private automobiles are of prime importance. Parking facilities should also be available. It might be advisable to prepare a small, simplified map and include it with the invitations or registration forms. Always stress the convenience of reaching the meeting and announce the parking facilities. In this respect, small meetings can be easily accommodated by motels which have meeting rooms and plenty of parking. Motels located near airports are special favorites with meeting organizers.

Picking the right hall

It is very important to match the size of the room to the number of people expected. A large audience in a small room is obviously a poor arrangement. However, the other extreme is also quite uncomfortable. A large, empty room with a small number of occupied chairs detracts from the prestige of the meeting and creates a dismal atmosphere. There is no simple formula for predetermining the amount of people that will attend a meeting. Therefore, in many cases it is desirable to obtain facilities that can be expanded. Most buildings suitable for meetings provide a simple arrangement of partitions used to enlarge the room. See Fig. 10-1.

The size of the room also obviously has something to do with the degree of comfort that it affords. Unless the air conditioning or heating is adequate, the size of the room must be considered. Thus, in a hot period, a small room packed to capacity with inadequate air conditioning will definitely make people miserable. An uncomfortable audience will pay little attention to the speaker.

Other aspects of physical comfort must be carefully considered. Make sure that you know where the air conditioning controls are, and that someone is available to man them during the meeting. Make sure that good ventilation is possible if no air conditioning is required. Many buildings shut off their plants during spring and fall, because of the comfortable temperature outside. Remember, however, that you have a packed room and that your audience's well-being is important.

The chairs must be comfortable for the duration of the meeting. They should, if possible, be noncreaking and suitable for taking notes. If extensive notes are required, consider using classroom-style tables. Whether or not tables are used, always make the spacing between rows adequate for comfort.

Not only the size but also the shape of the room must be considered. If a professionally designed auditorium is not available, any room could be utilized for a meeting. Figure 10-1 shows a typical arrangement in a rectangular room. Although this is not the only arrangement possible, experience has shown it to be very practical. Therefore, we will discuss it in some detail.

The room is rectangular and the speakers' stage is set up at the narrow side of the room, away from the door. It is important to have either a blank wall or curtained windows behind the speakers. This will prevent distraction of the audience and will also prevent light from getting in their eyes as they watch the speaker. The speakers' table and lectern are

Figure 10-1   Typical elongated room set up. (Note room partition and duplicate reception desk-sign location. These are used to enlarge room upon demand.)

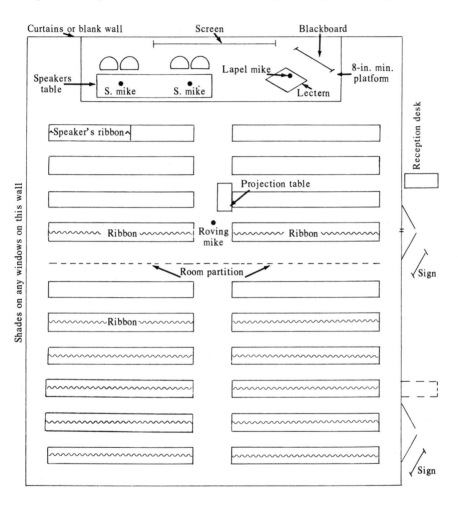

set up on a stage or platform at least eight inches high, as indicated. If no dignitaries or panelists are required, the speakers' table might be dispensed with. Note that on the left side of the first row (indicated with "speakers' ribbons"), places have been reserved for individuals who sit at the speakers' table. If a table is used on the stage and the lecture includes slides or other visual aids, these individuals might prefer to sit at the head of the room for the duration of the lecture. This arrangement will allow them to leave the speakers' table, around the corner, with the least possible confusion. They will thus not interfere with the projectionist, either.

The lectern is set up on the right-hand side of the speakers' table so that the lecturer can easily point to the screen. The latter is located in the middle of the room behind the panel table. From this location the speaker can also use the blackboard which is set on the extreme right of the stage for unexpected discussions and for the question-and-answer period.

Ideally, the stage is equipped with three individual microphones, two on the speakers' table so that any panel member can talk to the audience, and a lapel microphone rather than a stationary microphone for the lectern. A roving microphone which extends to the rear of the room is placed with the projectionist. This microphone is passed by him to the people wanting to ask questions or make comments from the floor. If this is not feasible, a stationary microphone is located behind the projectionist and the audience is asked to step up to the microphone in order to be heard. Without microphones, it is mandatory for the master of ceremonies to repeat each question.

Depending on the size of the room, the chairs are set up in straight lines for smaller rooms or in slightly slanted fashion for larger halls. In the smaller room, the aisle is in the center and a projectionist's table is slightly to one side of the aisle. See Fig. 10-1.

Sometimes the shape of the room does not lend itself to the aforementioned setup. In those cases, Fig. 10-2 shows another arrangement which is not quite as effective but which is adequate. Note that in this configuration, people sitting on both sides of the center row, especially in the front, might have trouble seeing the visual aids. The dashed line gives an outline of the maximum width of the room that can be used. Incidentally, in this setup a corner area has been set aside for display or for refreshments, as the case may be.

Ribbons should be placed on the rear chairs so that the audience will start filling the front rows first. The ribbons should be removed as the room fills up. The partition should be moved back and the room enlarged only when the room is nearly full. The outside door to the first room is locked after the door to the second room is opened. All ribbons are removed progressively until the entire audience is seated. This will eliminate the confusion in seating an audience. Many people prefer to sit in the back so that they can either fall asleep or get up in a hurry should

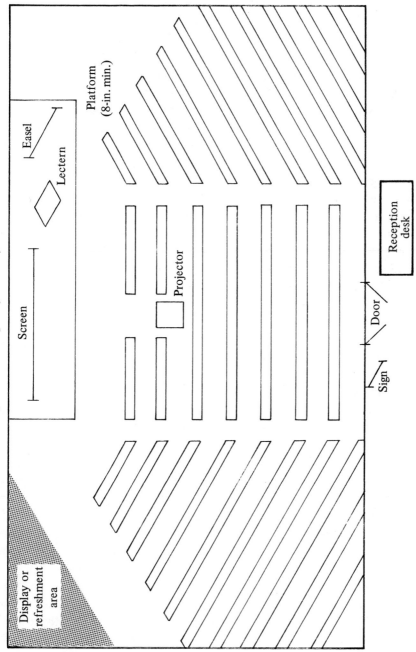

Figure 10-2 Alternate set-up. (Note that the space is not completely utilized.)

the lecture be a disappointment. This leaves unoccupied seats in the front which are not readily accessible to newcomers.

The lighting in the room must be easily controlled by the projectionist. A small light is required at the lectern which enables the speaker to follow his lecture cards. A dim light at the edges of the room should also be kept on at all times so that the room is not plunged into complete darkness during the lecture. This will help people in making notes and also will permit contact between the speaker and the audience. Finally, it serves to lessen the tendency of tired individuals to fall asleep. Care should be taken to avoid having any light (from the lectern or elsewhere) reflected off the screen. This must be checked beforehand when no slides are showing. Any reflected light will obviously affect the clarity of the visual aids. If there are any windows in the room, they must be shaded or curtained off during the daylight hours. Direct or indirect sunlight will diminish the effect of projected material. If neither slides nor films are used and only flip charts and similar visual aids are shown, these lighting considerations are less important. A spotlight on the display and a slight dimming of the room lights will help to focus audience interest. Under no circumstances should there be any lights blinding the speaker!

If registration or welcoming of the participants is planned, the reception table should be located outside the meeting room. Place it immediately in front of the door rather than inside. This will enable latecomers to register without distracting the meeting, which will in turn make things more comfortable for both the speaker and the latecomers themselves. It is always useful to appoint an usher or two in addition to the greeting committee. They will make it their business to help seat the people in the manner desired, remove ribbons as required, and generally make sure that all arrangements for the meeting are proceeding properly.

Signs must be planned ahead of time and properly located. These are the guideposts which direct the audience to the proper meeting room. They are essential when more than one meeting takes place in the same building. Remember that a well-prepared sign adds to the dignity of the meeting.

It is obvious that less-than-ideal conditions may sometimes exist. The ideally shaped room with the proper partitions cannot always be obtained. In cases where only large halls are available for relatively small assemblies, the number of chairs set up and the way in which they are set up must provide some intimacy between the speakers and the audience. The use of room dividers also enhances this effect. It might be wise to set up fewer chairs than will actually be used and have the ushers provide more chairs as the size of the audience increases. Try to avoid having many rows of empty seats in the back of the room. In this respect, ushers are extremely helpful in the proper seating of people. There is nothing more disappointing both to the speakers and the audience than a sparsely populated hall of large dimensions that gives the impression that the whole meeting was not worthwhile.

The need for a lapel microphone was indicated earlier in this chapter. This is particularly important when a speaker has acquired a style of his own. He will then not stand still in front of a stationary microphone. He may move around, point to his visual aids, move to the blackboard, etc. If no lapel microphone is provided, every movement of his head away from the stationary microphone will change his voice volume and detract from the material being presented. Stationary microphones are adequate for the panelists' table and in the audience itself. They can easily be used for the short duration of the questions and answers or comments. It is also well for the master of ceremonies and people making short speeches to use the lapel microphone in order to maintain the proper volume.

A note is in order here about the use of audio equipment in rooms of all sizes and about the taping of the proceedings. Unless the room is extremely small, it is advisable to plan on using a microphone. The speaker will not tire as easily as a result and the audience will be able to hear him throughout the room.

There is another advantage in this arrangement, in that it permits a recording of the meeting to be made. Special equipment can be easily incorporated into the audio system for this purpose. This is especially convenient if no printed proceedings of the conference will be available. Thus, people can purchase a copy of the recording and listen to the material later at their convenience. This is much cheaper than the printing process and has been tried successfully on several occasions. The only disadvantage in such a technique is the lack of the visual aids used in the meeting. These can usually be provided as a supplement to the record with the permission of the speakers.

When recording of the proceedings is contemplated, you must get the agreement of the speakers beforehand. Also, you should prepare signs indicating that "This meeting is being recorded," and place them at conspicuous places. You may find many people objecting to the recording and they might not want to speak or ask questions from the floor under these conditions.

Some other small matters must be discussed briefly. Make sure that the screen is large enough and takes up at least 20 percent of the wall space available behind the speaker or a maximum of 10 feet.

A pointer is required whenever a large screen is used. The speaker must be able to point to any items on the screen. A mechanical or optical pointer can be employed. For those who are not familiar with an optical pointer, it is simply a flashlight. The lens is blocked out, allowing

Figure 10-3 Checklist

1. Are the timing and location conducive to good attendance?
   a. Are there any rival meetings or conventions?
   b. Is transportation easy for most participants?
   c. Are parking facilities available (mentioned in program)?
   d. Is it necessary to include a map with the invitation?
2. Is the room appropriate for the audience size?
   a. Can the room be enlarged by opening partitions?
   b. Can additional chairs be set up later?
   c. Is the heating or air conditioning functioning and are you familiar with the location of controls?
   d. Are the seats comfortable and noncreaking?
   e. Will notes be taken? If so, larger spacing or tables are required.
3. Is the shape of the room suitable?
   a. Is a stage or portable platform available?
   b. Is there distraction on the wall behind the speaker (such as a window, etc.)?
   c. Is an aisle provided between the chairs?
   d. Is a projection table available?
   e. Is a speakers' or dignitaries' table required?
   f. Are microphones (lapel, stationary, roving) available?
   g. Are the switches to room lights easily accessible?
   h. Is there a lectern light, a dim background light, and no reflection off the screen?
4. Seating arrangements.
   a. Have a greeting committee and ushers been appointed?
   b. Is a speaker's ribbon required?
   c. Are ribbons for the rear rows available?
   d. Is a registration setup needed?
5. Are signs and the reception table set up?
6. Are a screen, a projector, and a pointer required?
7. Are a blackboard and chalk or lecture pad and pen needed?
8. Is water for the speakers available?
9. Are handout literature, name tags, etc., prepared?

a small concentrated beam in the shape of an arrow to strike the screen. Optical pointers are usually unsatisfactory, however, for two reasons: Unless the pictures or slides are relatively dark, the white light on white background does not show up too well. In addition, most speakers forget to turn off the light in the pointer. They keep on speaking, waving the flashlight in their hand. The tracings made by the pointer over the walls and ceilings usually cause a considerable amount of distraction. It is also possible for the light to be flashed at the audience and momentarily blind some of the listeners.

A blackboard equipped with chalk and an eraser is useful. Colored chalk and adequate cleaning equipment should always be considered a must. Proper lighting for the blackboard is also important. A large sketch block on an easel and "magic markers" can be used as a substitute.

Other items of importance include water on the speakers' table, name tags and identification cards for the audience, handout material, reprints, etc. These are all summarized in Fig. 10-3.

11 Organizing and Conducting a Technical Meeting

A discussion of technical presentations without a word on the organization of the entire meeting would be incomplete. You as the program chairman must prearrange the program to form an interesting continuity. Also, there are the little details of the art of chairing a meeting. All of this and more form the subject of this chapter.

Several parts of the meeting can be conducted without too much work on the part of the program chairman. Your contributions toward the success of the meeting depend on your paying attention ahead of time to such details as the proper introduction of the speakers, their subjects, and closing remarks. Let us first look at the type of work that is involved in the preparation of the program, the various types of meetings suitable for technical presentations, and finally, to the details of introducing the speakers, having the speaker write an introduction for himself, and the proper way to chair such a meeting.

The organization of a technical meeting

The organization of technical meetings is more difficult than one would think. It requires many arrangements which are time-consuming; in general, this is a thankless task. First, you have to obtain qualified speakers on related subjects. One of the worst offenses that you can commit in this area is the acquisition of papers that do not blend into a homogeneous program. You will also need one alternate paper in case of a no-show.

Then, you must make sure that these speakers prepare vital presentations. You should not allow them to read their papers. You also have to ensure that the written papers go to press on time.

Finally, before the meeting you must set up a briefing session. You will naturally be quite nervous until all of your speakers have assembled. You might require a last minute substitute in addition to your alternate speaker. In some cases you will have to fill in for a speaker who is absent. This is the time to formulate the introductions. Brief your speakers on the organization (procedures, timetable, etc.) of the meeting.

Now you are ready to lead the procession of speakers into the meeting hall. You should do this no more than fifteen minutes and not less than five minutes before the scheduled start of the program. If you are too early, your speakers will become nervous; if you are too late, your audience will be restless. Don't be too concerned about starting precisely on time. If many people are still arriving, use your judgment and wait a little.

When you get up to open a meeting, you should consider yourself as a first speaker of sorts. Prepare your opening remarks, rehearse them, and follow the guidelines suggested in the first part of this book. Get up to the lectern and address the audience. A simple statement like: "Ladies and Gentlemen" or "May I have your attention please" will serve to settle the listeners. Wait a few moments for everyone to sit down and stop talking. Then begin with your prepared greeting. Never start while people are still milling about. Try to avoid begging for silence; this creates a poor impression.

You should open with a greeting, acknowledging dignitaries, etc. (see "The Proper Personal Introduction," p. 46), i.e., "Fellow Society Members, Ladies and Gentlemen, Honored Guests . . . welcome to our annual meeting."

Now you should introduce yourself and state your assignment in the proceedings, i.e., "My name is John Doe and I am your program chairman for this evening."

Follow this by a statement of the subject to be covered and its purpose, i.e., "Our meeting tonight was organized to discuss the importance of . . . which is an urgent problem in our industry because. . . ."

The outline of the program is next. There you mention your speakers briefly by name, describe their topics in one sentence and elaborate a bit on the unity of the program, i.e., "We have a real group of experts for you tonight to review the subject from many viewpoints. Each one is a specialist in his field. Mr. A will cover . . . while Mr. B will cover . . . etc. So you see, we will consider this drug problem from the manufacturer's viewpoint, as well as from the patient's. We also felt that a legal opinion would be important and, of course, the medical aspects as seen by the doctors and hospital are an integral part. We feel sure that after you have heard all the divergent viewpoints of our speakers, you will be in a good position to form your own opinion."

This is the time to introduce your first speaker. Give his introduction as planned and then call him to the lectern (for further details, see page 48), shake his hand, help with the lapel microphone, and step away from the center of the stage. When he has completed his talk, go back and thank the speaker. Lead the applause. Then go into moderating the questions and answers or call on the next speaker.

You should always close the meeting with a summation. After the last speaker has finished and all questions have been answered, it is up to you to make the closing remarks. These are more difficult to prepare and a lot of spontaneous information must be added. You may want to take notes during the meeting. If you find this difficult, you might get by with a simple summation as follows:

"I am sure that you found this meeting as stimulating and informative as I did. Our speakers did a fine job of covering the field from all angles. I for one am going away from here with a lot of food for thought."

Several types of programs besides the rigid sequential reading of papers can be used to liven up the proceedings. These include panel discussions, cracker-barrel meetings, workshops, roundtables, etc. Very successful are prearranged technical sessions representing opposite viewpoints, and end up in discussion and rebuttal, with audience participation. Let us cover these, one by one, in order to help the prospective technical meeting chairman make the proper selection.

The Standard (Sequential) Meeting. The "standard" is the most common type of technical meeting. In it, the chairman introduces a number of speakers. They then present their material in turn. Normally, the subjects are in the same field but only remotely related and there is no special coordination among the speakers. The questions and answers are usually entertained by each speaker immediately after the talk. Many people will come for a specific talk and depart without listening to the rest of the program. This is, by far, the easiest type of meeting to organize. (It is usually unimaginative and hardly stimulating.) This is the format followed by most societies when large volumes of papers are presented during national conventions. Whenever the author is involved in this type of meeting, he cannot help but feel that he is in a busy marketplace.

To organize a standard meeting, most societies deem it sufficient for the technical chairman to solicit papers of general interest to the audience. The papers received are then arranged in some kind of sequence or grouping. Then, some societies insist upon prejudging the papers before acceptance. If the number of papers submitted is large and the time is short, some speakers are rejected. Normally, any even slightly promising paper is accepted and the number of simultaneous meetings is simply increased. This is not the best way to organize a meeting, however. You can easily avoid this pitfall, should you ever be a program chairman. Start out by having a firm idea of what your audience will be interested in and the level of their interest. When calling for papers, be specific about your theme for the meeting. Check out experts in this field and win them to your cause. You will thus have taken a big step toward success.

Next, screen the papers submitted, putting them to the test as outlined in Chap. 2. Pretend that each one is your own. One of the biggest hurdles, of course, is in trying to look beyond the written word at the author as a potential speaker. The success of your meeting depends on his contribution. It is your duty, therefore, to check him out. In a personal meeting or over the phone, ask if he knows that he cannot read his paper, but has to deliver a talk. Be specific about your minimum standards and see if he is still interested. You will be surprised how readily you can form an opinion after such contact, especially if you succeed in drawing him out. Only now should you select your roster of speakers. Don't worry too much about their stature; just make sure that they will be dynamic speakers. Obviously, their talks must blend in with one another and must conform to your concept of the meeting.

You should plan a coordination meeting with your speakers just prior to the program. Breakfast, lunch, or dinner is ideal for this purpose. Restate your goals and acquaint your speakers with the schedule. In some cases you may have to help them get over stage fright.

During the actual meeting, it is your duty to introduce each speaker in turn, giving a short biographical background of each and naming his respective talk. For further information on "Introduction to a Speaker," see Chap. 6. As mentioned earlier in this chapter, you should make some opening and closing remarks.

This type of meeting is resorted to less and less by the careful planners of good technical programs. For better audience reaction and participation, several other types of meetings are being arranged.

The Panel. In this type of meeting, a panel of five to seven experts is invited for a technical discussion on a specific subject. It is usual to open such a meeting with three or four panel members setting the tone through short talks. They introduce the topic of the day by presenting various viewpoints on the subject. The balance of the panel is then requested to talk for three to five minutes each. The floor is then opened for discussion. The speakers are usually limited to fifteen minutes each. This maintains a good time schedule. The panel moderator has an extremely important role in keeping the speakers from digressing.

If you are appointed as panel moderator, be sure to screen your panel members carefully. Make sure that they are really experts in the field. They must also be the type of people who can talk extemporaneously on any subject that may be brought up within the scope of the meeting. Of course, the subject for the meeting must be determined before the panel members are invited. Once this is done, you, the moderator, must find out the exact nature of each short speech. You must also invite the rest of the panelists to prepare a five-minute presentation to establish their area of specialty. You might ask them to expound their "pet peeves."

It is usual to have you, the panel moderator, present a ten-minute introductory or explanatory statement. You will also have to work continuously with the panel members toward the success of the meeting.

The longer talks should still be concise and to the point. The rest of the panel members in their five-minute presentations should be encouraged to contribute in something of a controversial manner so that a very lively discussion can get underway.

Here, the system of providing questionnaires (see Fig. 11-1) helps to organize the questions from the floor. These should be distributed among the audience beforehand. When filled out, they should be handed to an usher who continuously passes through the audience. The usher should then take these to you, the moderator. You must divide the questions into categories and assign them to the various speakers. It is a good idea to let the assigned panel members read the questionnaires, reflect upon their answers, and return the form with an indication of acceptance. Do not embarrass a panelist who might feel he does not have

Figure 11-1

SPONSORING SOCIETY
MEETING NAME
DATE & LOCATION

PANEL QUESTIONNAIRE

Addressed to: Entire panel☐ Specifically: Mr._____
Question:_____
(to be read to audience)

_____

_____

_____

_____

_____

Background information:_____
(for panel only; not to be reread)

_____

_____

_____

Name of inquirer:_____
Affiliation:_____

(For Moderator use only)

Assigned to: Panelists Mr._____ Yes ☐   No ☐
                    Mr._____ Yes ☐   No ☐
                    Mr._____ Yes ☐   No ☐
                    Mr._____ Yes ☐   No ☐

Moderator comments:_____

Sequence Number:_____

the ability to answer the question. It is also common courtesy to give the rest of the panel a chance to express its views. After the assigned speaker has completed his discussion, ask the other panel members if they have anything to add. If microphones are available on the floor, you would be wise to encourage comments from the audience. Many people in the audience may be able to add constructively to the subject.

As the moderator you should prepare beforehand a number of phrases to control the meeting. Use them to cut off any undesired bickering or belaboring of specific points for any subjects that do not hold the interest of the majority of listeners. Some choice examples in this area are given in Fig. 11-2.

Figure 11-2

1. "May I suggest that you discuss this problem further, in private, with Mr. X on the panel?"
2. "That is an excellent point, but may we come back to it later if time permits?"
3. "Since our time is limited we must adhere to the formal program ... perhaps we should consider your point for a further meeting."
4. "Because of the specific nature of your discussion, may we ask Mr. X to answer you in writing?"
5. "Since your question is outside the realm of this meeting, I'll have to ask you to hold your question."

For a panel-type setup, nameplates should be set before each panel member. Encourage the audience to address their questions to specific individuals. If it is your judgment as moderator, however, that the question should be answered by someone other than the person addressed, indicate this by saying, "I think this one can be easily answered by Mr. A on the panel, or in the audience, etc." Or, "In order to include Mr. A from the audience in our program, let's feed him this question." Or you might say, "Why don't we have Mr. A answer this from the floor since I know he has done work in this area."

You must be careful to look after the welfare of all panel members. It very frequently occurs that most of the questions are directed to part of the panel only. This might be the result of the type of material being presented and the information available to one or two of the speakers. It is also often the case that the more outspoken individuals on a panel tend to monopolize the proceedings. This is extremely embarrassing to other experts on the panel who might get no more than one or no questions. Being familiar with a different field, they will rightfully not volunteer any opinions in other areas. It is the duty of the moderator to encourage these people to participate. If there are no questions for them from the floor, use some prearranged questions. Before the meeting, jot down some topics agreed upon with each speaker. Introduce them in the following manner.

"And now, *I* have a question for Mr. B which, I am sure, the audience will feel is of general interest." And in this manner, it is easy to avoid embarrassing any one of the speakers on the panel. Of course, you can also pretend that you received the question in writing, saying, "I have a written question to Mr. B here. . . ."

All of this leads us to recognize that the preparation of a panel-type discussion requires a great deal of hard work. The subject must be appropriate. The speakers must know the central theme in advance and prepare their papers accordingly. Even the short comments of three-to-five-minutes duration must fit the pattern. As suggested earlier, they could follow a sequence such as "pet peeves" related to the topics. The speakers' background might serve as the unifying factor, starting each comment with, "My experience in this field has been. . . ."

The moderator must know his speakers and the audience. When questions are slow in coming from the floor, he must use the prearranged topics. These must encompass all speakers. In this way, the meeting is kept alive and does not have to be adjourned prematurely.

Finally, it is a good idea to have the panelists close the meeting with a few words which restate their views. In case of a discussion, they should use this to rebut their opponents' presentation. This serves as a nice summation but a good moderator should prepare a five-minute closing speech for himself. He should not only thank the participants on the panel and the speakers, but he should also review the highlights of the meeting. This will leave the audience with a clear idea of what was expressed during the meeting.

The best method of closing a meeting is with a round of applause. In addition to the psychological benefits, it lends to the closing an air of finality. The moderator should not leave this to a sponteneous reaction from the floor but should lead the applause at the end of his personal remarks of gratitude. A typical statement would be, "And now I would like the audience to join me on this note of 'thank you for a job well done' by giving our panel and all the participants on the floor a round of applause."

To summarize, let us review the panel meeting with an imaginary, suggested program, as shown in Fig. 11-3. Figure 11-4 is an actual program organized by the author. It was necessary here to acquire a moderator since a speaker should never double for this function.

The Cracker-Barrel Discussion. Anyone who is familiar with a "brainstorm session" within a company is aware of the benefits which

Figure 11-3   A typical program

---

1. Opening remarks by a dignitary (optional: approximately five minutes)
2. Introduction by technical chairman and/or panel moderator (approximately ten minutes) to cover:
   a. The subject of the panel meeting
   b. Personal introduction by name only of the panel members
   c. Full introduction of each individual speaker immediately prior to his paper
   d. Receive the questions and answers after each speaker's lecture (limited to approximately five minutes)
3. First speaker (approximately fifteen-twenty minutes)
4. Second speaker (approximately fifteen-twenty minutes)
5. Third speaker (approximately fifteen-twenty minutes)
6. Intermission,* coffee break, smoke period
7. Statement of panel procedure by the moderator (five minutes). Individual introduction to the panelists who have not yet spoken.
8. Fourth panelist's remarks (three-five minutes)
9. Fifth panelist's remarks (three-five minutes)
10. Sixth panelist's remarks (three-five minutes)
11. Seventh panelist's remarks (three-five minutes)
12. Answers to written questionnaires submitted, followed by queries from the floor** (time open according to program; not to exceed ninety minutes)
13. Introduce prepared questions, if time permits
14. Rebuttal by panelists to arguments of dissenting opinions expressed by various members of audience and panel
15. Closing remarks by moderator
    a. Summation of meeting (approximately five-ten minutes)
    b. Personal thanks to panel members
    c. Lead applause and close meeting

---

*An ideal time for first collection of questionnaires.
**If ushers are available, continue collecting questionnaires. In general, these are easier to answer than oral questions.

---

can be derived from this. Free discussion is used to crystallize an idea or to start action in a specific area. This technique can be easily applied to societies or industries by the old-fashioned cracker-barrel session.

A typical session is organized as follows. Three or four session leaders are selected beforehand to cover various aspects of the problem to be brainstormed. They prepare themselves a short, five-to-ten-minute opening statement aimed at their part of the program. A master of

Figure 11-4

As our technology becomes more advanced, the desire to gain better reliability at lower cost becomes more pronounced. In order to achieve higher reliability and still take advantage of the inherent economies when using soldering as the joining method, a thorough understanding of the underlying parameters is mandatory. Since solderability is truly the key to reliability when soldering, the following papers, which will be presented during this seminar, will delve deeply into the criteria required to achieve and maintain solderability. Various solderability tests will be discussed and actual case histories will be described.

Speakers

ROBERT NORTH
"Solderability"

RICHARD SWANSON
"Soldering for Reliability"

RUSSELL HANEY
"Insure Better Joint Reliability By Solderability Testing"

HOWARD MANKO
"Nondestructive Solderability Check:
A Key To Reliability and Economy"

Panel Discussion

DEAN DEAKYNE
Moderator

Note: Written questions for the panel should be submitted by May 10, 1966 to H. H. Manko, Alpha Metals, Inc., Jersey City, N. J.

Panel Members and Speakers

ALLEN, J.
Supervisor of Planning
General Electric Company,
Decatur, Illinois.

CLARNER, F.
Reliability Engineer, Delco Radio Division,
General Motors Corp., Kokomo, Indiana.

HANEY, R.
Manufacturing Development Engineer,
Delco Radio Division,
General Motors Corp., Kokomo, Indiana.

MANKO, H.
Director: Solder Research and Development,
Alpha Metals, Inc., Jersey City, New Jersey.

NORTH, R.
Chief Material Engineer, UNIVAC Plant No. 1,
St. Paul, Minnesota.

SWANSON, R.
Manager of Quality Assurance and Reliability Engineering,
Fabritek Corp., Amery, Wisconsin.

WEST, J.
Manager, Chemical Engineering, Magnavox Corp.,
Ft. Wayne, Indiana.

WILKIE, M.
Chief Engineer, Burgess Battery Co.,
Freeport, Illinois.

ceremonies is appointed to welcome the participants. After outlining the purpose of the meeting, he describes the three or four cracker-barrel sessions to be held and who their leaders will be. Each group leader is then invited to give his opening remarks before the full assembly. By this time, the audience is in a position to select one such section. The master of ceremonies then advises the participants as to where to go for the group discussion. Each individual group now meets with its appointed leader. These sessions last approximately one hour and are conducted in a relatively informal manner. This is followed by an intermission when the leaders of the various groups meet with the master of ceremonies to determine the exact time they will require for their report to the meeting at large. Coffee or refreshments are in the meantime being served to the audience. After the intermission, the leaders make their reports on the conclusions, findings, recommendations, and the general discussions which were held.

The meeting is usually closed by the master of ceremonies, who sums up the results. In some cases, a recommendation to the society at large may result. A vote is sometimes held on particular items.

An interesting example was a recent attempt by a technical society to cope with myriad government and military specifications. It was desirable to match them to the requirements of a particular industry. A cracker-barrel meeting was held which dealt with:

1. The meaning of the specifications to the industry.

2. Recommended revisions to the specifications.

3. A possible alternate specification which the industry should initiate.

The results of the meeting led to an industry proposal for revision. This was supported by documentation of tests run by individual companies. A round robin type of testing program was initiated to prove the advantages of the industry's revision.

The Workshop. A workshop is very similar to the cracker-barrel session. It has a central subject and usually involves audience participation. The term is applied to two different types of meetings. One type includes a demonstration, whereas the other centers around a discussion of specific topics by the participants.

One rewarding workshop of the first type has been organized by the author as part of a university seminar. It is scheduled for the evening between the two days of lectures. The workshop consists of equipment demonstrations by various manufacturers. The participants have been invited previously to bring parts and blueprints and to discuss their specific problems. A workshop, as such, gives the participants a chance to discuss, in private, problems which because of company policy they cannot discuss in public.

The more conventional workshop consists of a number of short addresses (five minutes each). These establish the individuals at the speakers' table as experts in a facet of the main subject. A moderator or master of ceremonies is required. His functions are very similar to those of the panel moderator. A quick comparison will reveal only minor differences between this type of workshop and the panel discussion. No formal speeches, and only an introductory address, are given. Also, in a workshop the speakers are usually of the same opinion, leaving little room for debate.

Since the workshop so closely resembles the panel discussion, the preparations for the two are very similar. They do not require repetition here. Just keep your aims in mind and select the experts in the field.

A word about scheduling the preparations

Now that you have seen the complexity of a meeting, consider the time element. When you get your appointment to organize a meeting, start right away. First you will want to draw up a program. Use the information presented earlier, and then make yourself a schedule. If you are familiar with PERT, use this method to map your arrangements.

The arrangements for any type of technical program are time-consuming. There is, for instance, the problem of printing the program. You can only draw it up after all of your speakers have been selected. You need their exact names, initials, titles, and sometimes a short biography, in addition to the correct title of each paper and an abstract. This might take weeks to get by mail. Try to avoid gathering such information by phone. It is not only expensive, but leaves room for many errors. Finally, you need all of the details for the meeting location, parking facilities, etc. After all the information is collected, you can draw up the program, but your troubles are not over. You will have to proofread the printers' plates and wait for the bulk printing. This seldom takes less than a month. If you plan to mail these, you might require a mailing service. Thus, you must prepare your program several months ahead. Figure 11-5 will serve as a good checklist to help you in your task. The times cited refer to the period required for all the preparations before the meeting. This is based on the author's experience. Under

Figure 11-5   Arrangements checklist

1. Hall details.
   a. Who will set up the room?
   b. When will it be available beforehand for inspection?
   c. Does it have:
      1. Enough chairs?
      2. Lectern with light and microphones?
      3. Speakers' table with water and microphones?
      4. Stage or platform?
      5. Screen and projection equipment?
      6. Blackboard or sketch pad?
      7. Registration facilities?
      8. Adequate signs?
2. Speakers' arrangements.
   a. Have you arranged meeting before the program?
   b. Do you have their hotel addresses if they are not local?
   c. Have you checked with them the night before?
   d. Do you know their needs in the way of visual aids?
   e. Do you have their personal introductions?
3. Other.
   a. Who will have registration duties?
   b. Who are the ushers?
   c. Who is the projectionist?

Figure 11-6   Estimated times needed for program organization

1. Acquiring your speakers
   a. Call for papers in magazines or society letters, etc.   ...8-12 months
   b. Canvassing the experts by mail   ...4-6 months
2. Developing the program
   a. Obtaining details from speakers (names, titles,
      manuscripts, etc.)   ...4-6 months
   b. Arranging for the hall (location, parking, food, etc.) ... 3 months
   c. Getting it printed for handout   ... 2 months
      and for mailing   ... 3 months
3. Sending out publicity
   a. Sending out news releases   ... 4 months
   b. Placing advertisements in magazines   ...3-4 months
   c. Placing advertisements in newspapers   ... 2 months

different circumstances this time might vary. You must check it out yourself. Remember, it is your meeting.

Make yourself a checklist specifically for your meeting. Include such details as are outlined in Fig. 11-6. Remember to insist on no cancellations, but accept substitutions (for speakers, ushers, etc.).

PART 3
Parliamentary Procedure

In the two previous sections of the book, we have dealt with speaker and audience relations in technical programs. However, there are many committee meetings and other similar technical sessions in which everyone, in a sense, is a speaker. These might take place within your own company or in outside activities. Such meetings in order to be a success must be run according to standard parliamentary procedure. Unfortunately, the average scientist and engineer is not properly schooled in this respect; and many meetings have a tendency to wander from the subject.

George Cavanaugh wrote Part 3 of this book specifically in an effort to present a practical down-to-earth guide through the maze of parliamentary procedures. I am sure you will find it helpful and useful in holding all future technical and committee meetings to schedule and to the subject. The rules will also come in handy if you are a working member of a committee and want to express yourself within its framework.

SIMPLIFIED PARLIAMENTARY PRACTICE*

George W. Cavanaugh R.P.

Registered Parliamentarian
National Association of Parliamentarians
Certified Professional Parliamentarian
American Institute of Parliamentarians

"The great purpose of all rules and forms is to subserve the will of the assembly rather than to restrain it; to facilitate and not to obstruct the expression of their deliberative sense."

12 *Be an Effective Parliamentarian*

INTRODUCTION

If you are a member of any deliberative body, whether it is a professional society, a lodge, a church group, a civic council, or a grange and you are confused about your rights as a member, perhaps you may find some of the answers here.

Do you belong to the so-called silent majority? Do you come away from meetings asking yourself these questions?

"I wonder if he had a right to say that?"

"Would I have been in order if I had said this?"

"I should have told them how I felt."

"I wanted to make a motion but didn't know how."

"I'm on a committee but don't know what I'm supposed to do."

"I had a feeling we were victims of a steam roller, but what chance does a minority have?"

If you have tried to find the answer to these questions in one of the more complex books on parliamentary procedure and have found yourself more confused than helped, if as a result of this investigation you decided the subject is too complex and ritualistic, then reading this section may prove helpful to you.

It is an attempt to approach the problem from a layman's point of view, leaving out as much of the formalities of procedure as is consistent with adequate and clear coverage of the subject. The author does not have any new formulas, does not feel that this is the answer to all questions, but only that this study may help to simplify somewhat a subject that so many people need to but do not understand.

Parliamentary law is a vital part of our way of living. All through our lives, from Johnnie's Cub Scouts to Grampa's Octogenarian Club, we all belong to one or more voluntary societies. It seems reasonable to assume that we should all have at least a fundamental knowledge of the rules that govern these organizations.

Whether the society is legislative or purely deliberative, the rules of the game are still basically the same. The reasoning behind this is obvious, since one of the basic ideals of democracy is the right of free speech. Accepting this fundamental principle from our constitution, it seems reasonable to have definite rules to guide the expressions of this right in deliberative assemblies. This is parliamentary law in action.

The main purpose of this section is to give a practical explanation of the essential rules of procedure in conjunction with the use of the Parliamentary Guide. In the author's opinion, if both the book and the Guide (p. 168) are used together, the end result will be a thorough understanding of all the parliamentary law that the average person will ever need. Because of this approach to the subject, the standard presentation has been abandoned. However, this more direct presentation should give quick, accurate answers to the layman looking for help.

As you go through these pages, think of the subject not as something complicated, but rather as a set of rules governing procedure, just as you have rules governing in any other activity. Study each motion in the book and refer to the Guide at all times. When the subject is understood, you may use only the Guide as a quick, accurate reference regardless of what motion may be on the floor. In this way you will always be completely at home in any parliamentary situation.

It should be pointed out here that the procedure found in this volume is entirely compatible with the standard teachings of parliamentary law. The basic rules of Thomas Jefferson, Luther Cushing, and Henry Robert are incorporated in the procedure on each motion in all the necessary essentials. The reader of this text may feel sure that what he learns here is sound, generally accepted teaching by all leading authorities on parliamentary law. The only difference here is an attempt at simplicity of presentation.

Some history

Parliamentary law is not new. It has roots that are deep in our civilization. History shows evidence of it in the meetings on the Hills of Abraham, in the councils of Athens, and in the famed Roman Senate. Even the ancient philosopher Aristotle mentions rules of procedure in his treatise on "Democracy." Mankind has always had rules to govern organizations; and man, as a social being, has since the beginning of time formed himself into societies.

What we might call modern parliamentary law had its origin in the British Parliament. Thomas Jefferson, when he was the first Vice President of the United States and thus the presiding officer of the Senate, compiled a set of principles and rules to guide the Senate in its deliberations. This first American parliamentary law book, known as "Jefferson's Manual," was based on the rules governing the British Parliament. The "Manual" is still the bible of all of our parliamentary practice.

The "Manual" was an excellent piece of work for legislative bodies, but it fell short of meeting the increasing need for rules of procedure for the many deliberative societies which were forming in the fertile soil of a free land. The opportunity of free speech and freedom of assembly which had been denied many of the immigrants in their homelands caused these societies to flourish.

Luther Cushing, an experienced lawyer who devoted his life to a study of parliamentary law, realized the great need for some sort of a guide for the deliberative bodies which were springing up so fast in this country. In 1845, Cushing published a volume called "Cushing's Manual" containing Jefferson's principles but written specifically for the use of voluntary organizations, that is, deliberative rather than legislative groups. He included in his work the common practices and procedure which had become part of the accepted rules of the voluntary organizations as a result of practical experience.

Although Cushing's work was a definite step toward bridging the gap between the legislative and the deliberative assembly proceedings, it remained for the third great American parliamentarian to define clearly just how voluntary societies should be ruled. In 1876 Major Henry M. Robert, United States Army Engineer, wrote a book of rules for the conduct of meetings which he advocated for the use of clubs of all kinds. He based his work on the Rules of Congress which were in turn based on

Jefferson's Manual and added rules of his own which he felt would help in the functioning of voluntary groups.

There is some disagreement among modern parliamentarians concerning Robert's famous Rules of Order. Many authorities are of the opinion that these rules specialize in techniques of obstruction and disagreement rather than rules to encourage harmony and efficiency in procedure. But whether you agree with all of his teachings or not, his Rules have been universally adopted by voluntary societies of all types. By causing people to be rule-conscious, he has made a great and lasting contribution to the parliamentary thinking of the entire English-speaking world.

More recently many parliamentarians have written books which have added to the general knowledge of this subject. Their works have been substantial improvements, for the most part, over the earlier writings. However, the basic teachings of Jefferson, Cushing, and Robert are evident in all the essentials of their treatises. It is somewhat like writing a book on religion—the Ten Commandments are always present as an underlying guide. In the same manner, Jefferson, Cushing, and Robert, in a parliamentary sense, remain as the guiding lights governing any treatise on proper procedure in a deliberative or legislative body.

A few fundamentals

There are two basic concepts behind all parliamentary law:
1. Freedom of speech
2. Two heads are better than one

To carry out these concepts, four fundamental functions must be followed:

1. The group must arrive at its intent. When a motion is passed, it should be the expression of the deliberative sense of the entire membership.

2. This is arrived at by a free and frank discussion in order to perfect the motion before voting.

3. The will of the majority always prevails.

4. The minority must be allowed to freely express their opinion.

The chairman

One of the most important things for a chairman to keep in mind is the old parliamentary advice, "The great purpose of all rules and forms is to subserve the will of the assembly rather than to restrain it; to facilitate and not to obstruct the expression of their deliberative sense."

In other words, it is much more important that the will of the majority be expressed than that strict adherence to all the niceties of parliamentary law be followed.

The chairman should be impartial, courteous and efficient.

Impartial. He must be entirely fair to each member. He is not a dictator, a judge, or in any way the final word. One of the easiest ways to completely disrupt any society is to play favorites. He should express no opinions on any subject except when he is working as a member of a committee. In this case, he has the same freedom of discussion as any other member.

Courteous. In a difficult situation in which a member is obviously wrong and is discussing a subject distasteful to the membership, the chairman should disregard this and give the member every courtesy. Even though the member is wrong, he is still entitled to fair treatment.

Efficient. He must have a basic knowledge of parliamentary procedure and know what the parliamentary situation is at all times. He should keep the membership informed as to what effect each motion will have if it is accepted or rejected. He should help those unaccustomed to parliamentary rules to properly phrase motions. He should keep the meeting moving at a proper rate so that it neither drags slowly nor moves so fast that important questions are not completely resolved. He should allow only one subject at a time. He should insist on members following the proper sequence of motions.

The chairman also has the responsibilities of presiding, calling the meeting to order, recognizing members, and using parliamentary rules.

Presiding. A good chairman will always make specific plans for each meeting. He should know the standard agenda and anticipate new business as much as possible. He should plan in advance any new committees or other appointments.

It is a good idea for a chairman to arrive at the meeting a little early. While waiting for the group to assemble, he may carry on informal discussion with the members. In this way, he may be briefed on important matters that are to be presented at the meeting.

Calling the Meeting to Order. The usual manner is for the chairman to rap the gavel and simply say, "The meeting will be in order."

Recognizing Members. A member must first rise and address the chair for recognition. In small groups and in committee meetings, this formality is not necessary. The chairman usually gives the maker of a motion the first opportunity of discussion since the one proposing a motion is the one most familiar with the subject. During the discussion he should call on members who are both for and against the motion as much as possible.

Using Parliamentary Rules. The chairman should use good judgment and use only as much formal procedure as is necessary so that the will of the majority is followed. He should not hesitate to allow minor infractions or even major ones if it is obvious that the decisions arrived at are unanimous. He should refrain from inflicting his knowledge of parliamentary law on the membership, keeping in mind that the expression of the deliberative sense and composite opinion of the group is much more important than parliamentary pyrotechnics.

Above all, he must remember that any member may appeal any of his decisions. The question of whether he is right or wrong is then decided by the judgment of the assembly.

13   *The Motions*

INTRODUCTION

A motion is a statement or expression of the opinion of a member presented for consideration and action of the assembly.

The proper presentation of a motion requires five steps:

1. A member rises and addresses the chair.
2. He is recognized by the chairman.
3. He states his motion.
4. It is seconded by another member.
5. It is then stated by the chairman to the assembly and is placed before the house for discussion if it is a debatable motion.

If a motion comes before the assembly in any other manner, it has been improperly presented; and it would be contrary to good practice to allow any discussion on it.

Correct terminology

Since a motion is a proposal that the assembly do certain things, it should be stated in that manner. "I move," meaning "I propose that," is the proper terminology for wording a motion. Anything else such as "I make a motion" or "I suggest" is not good form.

There must be no discussion of the motion when it is first made. Only after it is seconded by another member and stated by the chairman is it in order to discuss or debate the motion.

Proper presentation of a motion

Mr. Brown (rises and addresses the chairman): "Mr. Chairman."

Chairman: "Mr. Brown."

Mr. Brown: "I move that this society take sufficient money from its treasury to buy a new building."

Mr. Jones (without rising): "I second the motion."

Chairman: "It has been moved and seconded that this society take sufficient money from its treasury to buy a new building. Is there any discussion?"

The motion is now formally before the house for discussion.

Classification of motions

Motions are classified into four groups:

    I. Privileged
   II. Incidental
  III. Subsidiary
  IV. Main

Main Motion. Main or substantive motions are naturally the most important since their purpose is to bring before the assembly business which can then be discussed and acted upon.

Four so-called specific main motions are part of this family:

1. Reconsider
2. Rescind
3. Create orders
4. Take from the table

These motions are special ones which are handled the same as the regular main motions. It should be noted here that if there is no business before the house then any motion stated at that time becomes a main motion.

Subsidiary Motions. These motions are used to perfect, alter, or dispose of the main motion. Since they are directly connected with the main motion, it is in order to propose them while the main motion is being discussed.

The subsidiaries are:

Lay on the table
Previous question
Limit or extend debate
Postpone definitely

Commit
Amend
Postpone indefinitely

Incidental Motions. This group relates directly to the business at hand, and one incidental motion has no precedence over another. They are handled immediately as they are presented.

Incidental motions are:

Orders of the day
Point of order
Appeal
Suspension of rules
Object to consideration of the question
Information
Leave to withdraw a motion
Division of a question
Division of Assembly

Privileged Motions. These motions are emergency moves and have no particular relationship to the business before the house. Since they are matters of great urgency, they have high precedence which gives them the right to the floor above all the other groups.

The privileged motions are:

Adjourn
Recess
Question of privilege

Precedence of motions

Precedence of motions means the order in which motions may be presented, discussed, and disposed of. Since the incidental motions have no precedence among themselves, they present no problem.

Order of precedence following the Parliamentary Guide:
Privileged motions
1. Adjourn
2. Recess
3. Question of privilege
Subsidiary motions
13. Lay on the table
14. Previous question

15. Limit or extend debate
16. Postpone to a definite time
17. Refer to a committee
18. Amend
19. Postpone indefinitely
20. Main motion

There are two fundamental rules of precedence. When a motion is before the house (pending), any motion above it may be presented; and any motion below it may not be presented. For example, in the previous list of motions if No. 20, a main motion, is pending, it would be in order to propose No. 17, to refer to a committee. However, if No. 13, to lay on the table, is pending, it would be out of order to propose No. 18, to amend.

Example of Precedence. A member moves that the club hold its annual clambake on June 15. This main motion is No. 20 on the above precedence chart. While this motion is pending, another member moves to amend (No. 18) by changing June 15 to June 25.

While this amendment is being discussed, a member moves to refer the matter to a committee (No. 17). While the committee motion is being debated, another member moves to postpone consideration until the next meeting (No. 16).

At this point, a member moves to postpone indefinitely (No. 19). The chairman informs the member that the motion is out of order because it is below the pending motion in order of precedence.

A member now rises and asks a question of privilege (No. 3). The chairman asks what his question is, and the member asks if the windows may be closed since the noise from the street prevents him from hearing the discussion.

Now before the house are the following:

Question of privilege (No. 3)
Postpone definitely (No. 16)
Refer to a committee (No. 17)
Amend (No. 18)
Main motion (No. 20)

The chairman first decides on the request to close the windows. The motion then before the house is No. 16 (postpone definitely). If this motion is lost, he states the next motion (No. 17) (to refer to a committee). If this is lost, he considers No. 18 (to amend) and finally

No. 20 (the main motion). Obviously, if either postpone or refer is passed, the main motion is temporarily disposed of.

In the event of several motions before the house at the same time, it is the duty of the chairman to keep the assembly informed so that they have a clear picture of the parliamentary situation at all times.

General rules applying to all motions

Can a motion interrupt a speaker? Because of their urgency or because time is critical, there are a few motions which may interrupt a speaker. If they are not proposed immediately, it becomes too late for them to receive consideration.

These motions are given below:
1. Reconsider
2. Object to consideration
3. Appeal
4. Division of assembly
5. Point of order
6. Question of privilege
7. Information
8. Orders of the day

Does the motion require a second? Generally speaking, all motions require a second. This rule is based on the principle that there should be at least two members of the assembly interested in the proposed motion. However, there are many actions that are in the request or inquiry class that do not require a second. These questions, such as point of order, are not technically motions and therefore a second is not required.

Can a motion be amended? The general rule governing amendment is simply that if a motion can be varied it can be amended. For example, point of order obviously cannot be stated any other way and is not amendable. Recess can vary from five minutes to five hours and, thus, is amendable.

Is the motion debatable? A simple rule to follow is that if it is necessary to discuss a motion before it is decided, it becomes debatable. Thus, all motions (questions, inquiries) of a procedural nature are not debatable because a discussion is not necessary to decide them.

Does the motion require two-thirds or a majority? The motions requiring a two-thirds vote are those that affect the rights of the minority.

These motions include:

Previous question
Limit or extend debate
Objection to consideration
Suspension of rules

If one more than a third are opposed to these motions, the minority can vote them down and preserve its rights. In this manner, the majority is prevented from using steamroller tactics.

Nominations and elections

Nominations. Most organizations either appoint or elect a nominating committee which usually lists one candidate for each office. At the meeting at which the election is to take place, the chairman of the nominating committee reports the list of nominees. The chairman of the meeting then asks for nominations from the floor for each office.

Since a nomination is not technically a motion, it is not necessary to have a second. However, many societies still follow the plan of calling for a second.

Example.

Chairman: "I now call on Mr. Brown for the report of the nominating committee."

Mr. Brown: "Mr. Chairman."

Chairman: "Mr. Brown."

Mr. Brown: "The nominating committee met and after due study submitted the following lists of candidates." (Name them.)

Chairman: "Thank you, Mr. Brown. You have heard the report of the nominating committee. Nominations from the floor are now in order. Are there any other nominations for president?"

Mr. Smith: "Mr. Chairman."

Chairman: "Mr. Smith."

Mr. Smith: "I nominate Mr. Black."

Chairman: "Are there any other nominations?"

This method is followed until all the nominations are completed. The polls may then be closed by a two-thirds vote; or if there are no additional nominations, the chairman may assume unanimous consent and not conduct a formal vote.

Elections. Standard practice dictates the use of a majority vote for election. This may be arrived at by voice vote, standing vote, roll call vote, or secret ballot. If no candidate has a majority, then the candidate receiving the smallest number of votes is eliminated; and the vote is retaken. This method continues until one candidate receives a majority. In this situation a majority means more than half of all the legal votes cast.

1—Adjourn—1

Purpose. To terminate a meeting.

Example.

Member: "Mr. Chairman," (wait for recognition) "I move we adjourn."

Another member: "I second the motion."

Chairman: "It is moved and seconded that we adjourn. All those in favor of adjournment say 'I'." (Wait for vote.) "Those opposed say 'no'." (Check vote.)

If "I" vote has the majority the chairman says: "The 'I's' have it. The motion to adjourn is carried. The meeting is adjourned." (Strike gavel.)

If "no" vote has majority the chairman says: "The 'no's' have it. The motion to adjourn is lost." The chairman continues with the business of the meeting.

Points to Remember. An unqualified adjourn motion takes precedence over all other motions.

If qualified (e.g., "I move we adjourn at six o'clock."), the motion has no privilege and is treated the same as a main motion.

If no time has been set for the next meeting and if adjournment, if passed, would mean the dissolving of the assembly, then it becomes a main motion. This means it is debatable, amendable, etc.

It may be renewed after progress in the business of the meeting.

When unqualified, it can have no other motions applied to it.

It is not always in order. Cannot be made when a question has been put to a vote, and the vote is being taken.

Answers to the Eight Fundamental Questions Concerning a Motion to Adjourn.

Can it interrupt a speaker?	No
Does it require a second?	Yes
Is it debatable?	No
Is it amendable?	No
Is a vote required?	Majority
It only applies to what?	No motions
What can be applied to it?	No motions
Is it renewable?	Yes

2—Recess—2

Purpose. To have a brief intermission in the meeting.

Example.

Member: "Mr. Chairman," (wait for recognition) "I move we recess for" (state time of recess or duration and reasons for calling recess).

Another member: "Mr. Chairman, I second the motion."

Chairman: "It is moved and seconded that the meeting recess until" (state time, etc.). "All those in favor of recess say 'I'." (Wait for vote.) "Those opposed 'no'." (Check vote.)

Depending on the vote, the chairman either calls a recess or continues with the business of the meeting.

Points to Remember. The functioning of the motion to recess is generally the same as to adjourn.

If the motion is adopted, the meeting is temporarily interrupted until the time specified. When it reconvenes, business is again conducted as if there had been no interruption.

Adjourn is used to end a meeting until the next regular session.

Recess is used to interrupt a meeting for a short period of time with it reconvening on the same day.

Answers to the Eight Fundamental Questions.

Can it interrupt a speaker?	No
Does it require a second?	Yes
Is it debatable?	No
Is it amendable?	Yes
Is a vote required?	Majority
It only applies to what?	No motions
What can be applied to it?	Amend
Is it renewable?	Yes

3—Question of privilege—3

Purpose. Take care of the comfort, safety, and convenience of the individual members and the assembly as a whole.

Example.

Member: "Mr. Chairman," (not waiting for recognition) "I rise to a question of privilege."

Chairman: "Please state your question."

Member: "I request that the windows be closed so that we in the back of the hall can hear the speaker."

Chairman: "Your request is granted. Will someone please close the windows."

When a question of privilege is made in the form of a motion, it loses its high rank and becomes a debatable question subject to all the rules of a main motion.

A motion of privilege would be a situation in which a debatable matter might be brought up.

Example.

Member: "Mr. Chairman, I rise on a question of privilege. I move that all the non-members present leave the hall until the business part of our meeting has been concluded."

Another member: "Mr. Chairman, I second the motion."

Chairman: "It is moved and seconded that the non-members leave the hall until the business part of our meeting has been concluded. Is there any discussion?"

After discussion, if any, the motion goes to a vote in the usual manner. If it is passed, the chairman takes the necessary action and then directs the assembly back to the pending motion.

Points to Remember. As a question of privilege it takes precedence over all motions except recess and adjourn.

As a motion of privilege, it has no special precedence.

It may interrupt a member speaking if there is an urgent need.

All questions are decided by the chairman and any member of the assembly has the right of appeal.

Examples of questions of privilege are noise in the hall, poor heating or ventilation, personal threats or attacks, illness, etc.

Answers to the Eight Fundamental Questions.

Can it interrupt a speaker?	Yes
Does it require a second?	No
Is it debatable?	No
Is it amendable?	No
Is a vote required?	None
It only applies to what?	No motions
What can be applied to it?	No motions
Is it renewable?	No

4—Orders of the Day—4

Purpose. Request chairman to follow planned program of business.

Example.

Member: "Mr. Chairman," (not waiting for recognition) "I call for the order of the day."

Chairman: "If there is no objection, the order of the day will now be handled."

This call could refer to an insistence on the normal procedure of the society or to consideration of a matter postponed to this meeting (general order) or to a motion scheduled for a particular time during this meeting (special order).

If a special order is called for at the proper time, it must be considered unless it is postponed by a two-thirds vote.

A general order may be postponed only by a majority vote.

Points to Remember. Takes precedence over all motions except questions of privilege, recess, and adjourn.

Since it is technically not a motion, it does not require a second and is not debatable or amendable.

Answers to the Eight Fundamental Questions.

Can it interrupt a speaker?	Yes
Does it require a second?	No
Is it debatable?	No
Is it amendable?	No
Is a vote required?	None
It only applies to what?	No motions
What can be applied to it?	No motions
Is it renewable?	No

5—Point of order—5

Purpose. To correct a violation of the rules on the part of either a member or the chairman.

Example.

Member: "Mr. Chairman," (not waiting for recognition) "I rise to a point of order."

Chairman: "State your point of order."

Member: "I make the point of order that the proposed amendment has no connection with the main motion."

Chairman: "Your point of order is well taken. The proposed amendment is out of order." The assembly then returns to the pending business.

Points to Remember. Any member can make a point of order.

It can be made at any time, even when another member is speaking.

It must be made promptly at the time violation occurs.

If any member is not satisfied with the ruling of the chair, he may appeal the decision of the chair. In this case the final decision is made by the assembly.

If the chairman is in doubt about a ruling, he may refer it to the parliamentarian (if the society has one); or he may refer the vote to the assembly for its decision.

It does not require a second and is not debatable.

Answers to the Eight Fundamental Questions.

Can it interrupt a speaker?	Yes
Does it require a second?	No
Is it debatable?	No
Is it amendable?	No
Is a vote required?	None
It only applies to what?	Any errors
What can be applied to it?	No motions
Is it renewable?	No

6—Appeal the decision of the chair—6

Purpose. To reverse the ruling of the chair.

Example.

Member: "Mr. Chairman," (not waiting for recognition) "I appeal the decision of the chair."

Another member: "Mr. Chairman, I second the motion."

Chairman: "An appeal from the decision of the chair has been moved and seconded. Is the opinion of the chair sustained? Is there any discussion?" Chairman must allow sufficient time for proper discussion.

If the "I" vote has the majority, "The 'I's' have it, and the decision of the chair is sustained."

If the "no" vote has the majority: "The 'No's' have it, and the decision of the chair has been reversed by the assembly."

By use of this motion, any member may formally disagree with a ruling of the chair on a point of order, information, or privilege. In fact any opinion the chair makes may be contested.

Points to Remember. The chairman does not actually enter into debate on the question, but he may explain why he made the particular ruling that is being questioned.

It yields to the privileged motions.

It requires a second and is in order even when another motion has the floor.

Motions to lay on the table and previous question may be applied to it.

A tie vote on the appeal sustains the decision of the chair.

Motion must be made immediately after the ruling by the chair.

Answers to the Eight Fundamental Questions.

Can it interrupt the speaker?	Yes
Does it require a second?	Yes
Is it debatable?	Yes
Is it amendable?	No
Is a vote required?	Tie or majority
It only applies to what?	Decision of chair
What can be applied to it?	Lay on table
	Previous question
	Limit or extend debate
	Postpone definitely
	Reconsider
Is it renewable?	No

7—Suspension of rules—7

Purpose. To temporarily set aside whatever rules interfere with the proper consideration of a pending motion.

Example.

Member: "Mr. Chairman," (wait for recognition) "I move to suspend the rule limiting debate to five minutes; otherwise the motion will not be properly discussed."

Another member: "Mr. Chairman, I second the motion."

Chairman: "It is moved and seconded that we suspend the rule which limits debate to five minutes."

"Those in favor of suspending this rule say 'I'." (Wait for vote.)

"Those opposed to the suspension of this rule say 'no'." (Check vote.)

If the "I" vote has two-thirds majority: "The 'I's' have it, and the motion to suspend this rule is carried."

If the "no" vote has more than one-third: "The 'no's' have it, and the motion to suspend the rule is lost."

Points to Remember. Only rules of order, special, or standing rules may be suspended.

This motion does not refer to the basic constitution or by-laws.

To change these fundamentals requires previous notice and the proper amendment.

Takes precedence over main and subsidiary motions.

Yields to privileged motions.

Cannot be debated or reconsidered.

Answers to the Eight Fundamental Questions.

Can it interrupt a speaker?	No
Does it require a second?	Yes
Is it debatable?	No
Is it amendable?	No
Is a vote required?	Two-thirds
It only applies to what?	No motions
What can be applied to it?	No motions
Is it renewable?	Yes

8—Object to consideration—8

Purpose. To prevent the assembly from considering a question.

Example.

Member: "Mr. Chairman, (not waiting for recognition) I object to the consideration of this motion."

Chairman: "There is an objection to the consideration of this motion. Those in favor of considering this question say 'I'." (Wait for vote.) "Those opposed to considering this question say 'no'." (Check vote.)

If "I" vote has more than one-third: "The 'I's' have it. The motion will be considered."

If the "no" vote has two-thirds: "The 'no's' have it. The motion (state motion) will not be considered."

If the "I" vote is carried, the motion in question is considered as usual.

If the "no" vote is carried, the chairman directs the assembly to the next order of business.

Points to Remember. This motion is made when a question is brought up which most members feel is unnecessary, embarrassing, unimportant, or not presented at the proper time.

Applies to main motions only.

Must be made immediately after the motion is moved.

If any discussion takes place, it is too late to make this motion.

Requires a two-thirds vote to prevent consideration.

If a minority of one more than one-third want to consider it, the motion is handled in the usual manner.

In order to protect the minority who wish the motion to be considered, the chairman should not allow the motion to lay on the table to be made until some discussion has taken place.

Answers to the Eight Fundamental Questions.

Can it interrupt a speaker?	Yes
Does it require a second?	No
Is it debatable?	No
Is it amendable?	No
Is a vote required?	Two-thirds
It only applies to what?	Main motion
What can be applied to it?	No motions
Is it renewable?	No

9—Point of information—9

Purpose. To clarify a question concerning the meaning or application of the rules of order or the specific rules governing the organization.

Example.

Member: "Mr. Chairman," (not waiting for recognition) "I rise to a point of information."

Chairman: "Please state your question."

Member: "Would it be in order for me to move to postpone consideration of this motion to the next meeting?"

Chairman: "This motion is in order." Under this motion, "rising to a point of parliamentary inquiry" is handled in the same manner. Both motions have the same purpose—the difference is only in the terminology.

Points to Remember. Very often members are confused as to what the Parliamentary situation is at the moment. When an inquiry is made, it becomes the duty of the chairman to explain to the member what the proper procedure is.

All such requests must be made directly to the chair. No member has the right to direct his remarks to another regardless of what the question is.

If a member continues to ask questions that are obviously dilatory and are obstructing normal business, the chairman should not entertain such motions.

Answers to the Eight Fundamental Questions.

Can it interrupt a speaker?	Yes
Does it require a second?	No

Is it debatable?	No
Is it amendable?	No
Is a vote required?	None
It only applies to what?	No motions
What can be applied to it?	No motions
Is it renewable?	No

10—Withdraw a motion—10

Purpose. The mover of a motion wants to stop its consideration.

Example.

Member: "Mr. Chairman," (wait for recognition) "I request permission to withdraw my motion."

Chairman: "Mr. Brown requests leave to withdraw his motion. If there is no objection the motion will be withdrawn."

If there is an objection to withdrawing the motion, any member may rise and make this motion. "Mr. Chairman, I move that Mr. Brown be allowed to withdraw his motion."

Chairman: "It is moved that Mr. Brown be allowed to withdraw his motion. Those in favor say 'I'." (Wait for vote.) "Those opposed say 'no'." (Check vote.)

If the 'I' vote has a majority: "The 'I's' have it. Mr. Brown has permission to withdraw his motions."

If the 'no' vote has a majority: "The 'no's' have it and the request to withdraw the motion before the assembly is denied. Is there any further discussion on Mr. Brown's motion?" (State the motion in question.)

Points to Remember. The mover of a motion has complete control over it until the time it is stated by the chair. Until then, he is free to withdraw it or change it at his own discretion.

After it is stated by the chair, it becomes the property of the assembly. If they object to allowing the mover to withdraw it, a motion is necessary to decide the question.

The examples given here assume that the motion has been stated by the chair and is being debated.

Answers to the Eight Fundamental Questions.

Can it interrupt a speaker?	No
Does it require a second?	No
Is it debatable?	No
Is it amendable?	No

Is a vote required?	Majority
It only applies to what?	All motions
What can be applied to it?	No motions
Is it renewable?	Yes

11—Division of a question—11

Purpose. Request the assembly to divide a motion which is composed of two or more independent parts into individual motions which may then be voted on separately.

Example.

Member: "Mr. Chairman," (wait for recognition) "I move that the society have its annual dinner in January and that the dues be raised to ten dollars."

Another member: "Mr. Chairman, the proposed motion seems to contain two separate ideas. I move that the question be divided and each proposition be voted on individually."

Chairman: "It is requested that the motion be divided into two parts. If there is no objection, this will be done.

"The motion to be first considered is that the society shall have its annual dinner in January. Is there any discussion?"

The second part concerning the dues is then taken up.

Points to Remember. A member may request a division in the following instances:

(*a*) When a motion has more than one main proposition

(*b*) When a committee report containing many different recommendations is presented

No matter how complicated a question is, it cannot be divided unless it contains more than one distinct proposition.

Answers to the Eight Fundamental Questions.

Can it interrupt a speaker?	No
Does it require a second?	No
Is it debatable?	No
Is it amendable?	No
Is a vote required?	None
It only applies to what?	Main motion and motion to amend
What can be applied to it?	No motions
Is it renewable?	No

12—Division of Assembly—12

Purpose. To request a more accurate count when there is doubt about the results of a voice vote or a vote by show of hands.

Example.

Member: "Mr. Chairman," (not waiting for recognition) "I call for a division."

Chairman: "A division is called for. In order to have a more accurate count will those in favor of the motion please stand." (Count members standing.) "Be seated.

"Now those opposed please stand." (Count.) "Be seated."

If the chairman is in doubt himself, he should on his own initiative ask for a division and take another count. This situation develops only when the vote is taken by voice (sound) or show of hands.

Obviously, if the vote is taken by ballot, no problems of this type exist. If a member wishes for the sake of accuracy to have a ballot vote, he so moves.

Example.

Member: "Mr. Chairman," (not waiting for recognition) "I move the vote on this question be taken by ballot."

Another member: "I second the motion."

Chairman: "It is moved and seconded that the vote on this question be by ballot.

"Those in favor of voting by ballot say 'I'." (Wait for vote.)

"Those opposed to voting by ballot say 'no'." (Check vote.)

If "I" vote has a majority: "The 'I's' have it and the motion to vote by ballot is carried." The chairman then appoints tellers to handle the ballots.

If "no" vote has a majority: "The 'no's' have it and the motion to vote by ballot is lost." The chairman continues with the next order of business.

Points to Remember. Very often in large assemblies, it is almost impossible to take a *viva voce* vote accurately. The simple methods of having each group stand or, if necessary, of dividing the groups on opposite sides of the hall usually solves the problem. Vote by roll call or ballot is obviously the most accurate method. This should be followed on the more important matters, particularly in large assemblies.

Answers to the Eight Fundamental Questions.

Can it interrupt a speaker?   Yes

Does it require a second?	No*
Is it debatable?	No
Is it amendable?	No
Is a vote required?	None*
It only applies to what?	Voice or show of hand votes
What can be applied to it?	No motions
Is it renewable?	No

13—Lay on the table—13

Purpose. To set aside consideration of a motion until a later but undetermined time.

Example.

Member: "Mr. Chairman," (wait for recognition) "I move to lay the motion on the table."

Another Member: "Mr. Chairman, I second the motion."

Chairman: "It is moved and seconded that we table the motion to . . . ." (Repeat the motion referred to.)

"Those in favor of tabling the motion say 'I'." (Wait for vote.)

"Those opposed say 'no'." (Check vote.)

If "I" vote has a majority: "The 'I's' have it and the motion to . . . (repeat the motion) is tabled." The chairman continues with the order of business.

If "no" vote has a majority: "The 'no's' have it and the motion to table is lost."

The chairman explains that the original motion is still before the house for discussion.

Points to Remember. Can apply only to main motions, amendments, and appeals.

Takes precedence over all subsidiary motions.

Cannot be debated or amended.

There are several reasons why lay on the table might be desirable to the membership.

1. Those who are opposed to the motion may want to put it aside without allowing debate.
2. Those in favor of the motion may doubt their chances of carrying the motion and want time to promote more votes.

*Yes in case of motion to vote by ballot.

3. The assembly may think the question is too involved to decide hurriedly, and in this way more time for consideration is given.

4. More important matters may be considered first.

A motion which has been tabled becomes null and void if it is not taken from the table at the same meeting or the next regular meeting. This refers to societies that meet at least quarterly.

Answers to the Eight Fundamental Questions.

Can it interrupt a speaker?	No
Does it require a second?	Yes
Is it debatable?	No
Is it amendable	No
Is a vote required?	Majority
It only applies to what?	Appeal, amend, and main motions
What can be applied to it?	No motions
Is it renewable?	Yes

14—Previous question—14 (Vote immediately)

Purpose. To initiate an immediate vote on the question or questions before the assembly without further discussion.

Example.

Member: "Mr. Chairman," (wait for recognition) "I move the previous question." (If there are several motions on the floor, he may move the previous question on one or all the pending motions.)

Another Member: "Mr. Chairman, I second the motion."

Chairman: "The previous question has been moved and seconded.

"All those in favor of closing debate and voting immediately say 'I'." (Wait for vote.)

"Those opposed say 'no'." (Check vote.)

If the "I" vote has two-thirds: "The 'I's' have the necessary two-thirds vote and the previous question is carried." The chairman then directs the assembly to an immediate vote on the original motion or amendment or whatever the previous question was moved on.

Chairman: "Those in favor of (whatever the pending motion is) say 'I'." (Wait for vote.)

"Those opposed say 'no'." (Check vote.)

Points to Remember. To avoid confusion with the terminology, it must be kept in mind that previous question simply means stop debate and vote immediately.

Takes precedence over all subsidiary motions except lay on the table.

If it is moved without specifically indicating which motion or motions it should be applied to, its effect is confined to the immediately pending question. In other words, the mover of the motion should specify what motion or motions he has in mind.

The motion to lay on the table may be made while previous question is pending. The effect of this motion if passed is to lay the main motion with all the other pending motions on the table.

Cannot be debated or amended.

A two-thirds vote is required because a restriction of debate is contrary to the fundamental principle of parliamentary law, i.e., free and frank discussion of each motion.

Answers to the Eight Fundamental Questions.

Can it interrupt a speaker?	No
Does it require a second?	Yes
Is it debatable?	No
Is is amendable?	No
Is a vote required?	Two-thirds
It only applies to what?	Debatable motions
What can be applied to it?	No motions
Is it renewable?	Yes

15—Limit or extend debate—15

Purpose. To limit debate is to restrict the time allowed for discussion of a motion. To extend debate is to change or entirely remove rules restricting debate in order to increase the discussion time.

Example.

Member: "Mr. Chairman," (wait for recognition) "I move that debate be limited to three minutes," or "I move that time allowed to each speaker be extended to ten minutes."

Another Member: "Mr. Chairman, I second the motion."

Chairman: "It is moved and seconded that the debate be limited to three minutes" (or that it be extended to ten minutes).

"Those in favor say 'I'." (Wait for vote.)

"Those opposed say 'no'." (Check vote.)

If "I" vote has two-thirds: "The 'I's' have it by a two-thirds vote, and the motion to limit debate" (or extend it) "is carried." Chairman directs assembly to the continuation of the discussion.

If "no" vote has more than one-third: "The 'no's' have it by more than one-third and the motion to limit debate (or extend it) is lost."

The chairman continues with discussion on the motion before the house.

Points to Remember. A two-thirds vote is required because:

(*a*) The motion to limit debate may interfere with one of the basic concepts of parliamentary law, i.e., a full, free and frank discussion of each motion.

(*b*) A motion to extend debate means removing or modifying restrictions already imposed.

Since the time in the motion can be varied, the motion is amendable.

Answers to the Eight Fundamental Questions.

Can it interrupt a speaker?	No
Does it require a second?	Yes
Is it debatable?	No
Is it amendable?	Yes
Is a vote required?	Two-thirds
It only applies to what?	Debatable motions
What can be applied to it?	Amend
Is it renewable?	Yes

16—Postpone definitely—16 (Postpone to a certain time)

Purpose. To postpone discussion of the pending motion to a future date and usually to fix the time for its further consideration. A question postponed in this manner becomes an order of the day for that meeting.

Example.

Member: "Mr. Chairman," (wait for recognition) "I move we postpone consideration of this motion until the next meeting," or "until Thursday at five o'clock," or "until after the Mayor's speech at the next monthly meeting."

Another Member: "Mr. Chairman, I second the motion."

Chairman: "It is moved and seconded that we postpone consideration of this motion until the next meeting" (or one of the other times suggested). "Is there any discussion?" (Chairman must allow sufficient time for proper discussion.)

"Those in favor of the motion to postpone definitely say 'I'." (Wait for vote.)

"Those opposed say 'no'." (Check vote.)

If "I" vote has a majority: "The 'I's' have it and the motion to postpone definitely is carried." The chairman takes up the next order of business.

If "no" vote has a majority: "The 'no's' have it and the motion to postpone definitely is lost."

The chairman directs the assembly back to discussion of the motion.

Points to Remember. A standard postponement to a future meeting requires a majority vote.

If a specified time during the next meeting for consideration of the motion is made, then it becomes a special order and requires a two-thirds vote.

Applies only to main motions. However, any subsidiaries pending are postponed with the main motion.

Takes precedence over motions to commit, amend, and postpone indefinitely.

It is debatable and amendable with restrictions. It must be confined to the time of postponement or the advisability of postponement.

Answers to the Eight Fundamental Questions.

Can it interrupt a speaker?	No
Does it require a second?	Yes
Is it debatable?	Yes
Is it amendable?	Yes
Is a vote required?	Majority
It only applies to what?	Main motions
What can be applied to it?	Previous question
	Limit or extend debate
	Amend
Is it renewable?	Yes

17—Refer to a committee—17

Purpose. To designate a small group either by appointment or election to consider, investigate, or take action upon some matter of business and report their recommendations to the assembly for its further consideration.

Example.

Member: "Mr. Chairman," (wait for recognition) "I move this question be referred to a committee." The committee members may be designated by name or the maker of the motion may say, "be referred to a committee to be appointed by the chair."

Another Member: "Mr. Chairman, I second the motion."

Chairman: "It is moved and seconded that the motion (state it) be referred to a committee (specify how it is to be chosen). Is there any discussion on this matter?" (Chairman must allow sufficient time for proper discussion.)

"Those in favor of having this motion referred to a committee" (again state the manner of how the committee is to be chosen) "say 'I'." (Wait for vote.)

"Those opposed say 'no'." (Check vote.)

If the "I" vote has a majority: "The 'I's' have it and the motion to refer to a committee is carried." The chairman either appoints the committee members if that was the intent of the motion, or he names the members who were designated in the motion.

If "no" vote has a majority: "The 'no's' have it and the motion to refer to a committee is lost."

The chairman then explains that the business before the house is the continued discussion of the pending motion.

Points to Remember. Besides the two methods already mentioned of either having the chairman appoint committee members or designating them by name, they may also be elected in the usual manner. This latter method is sometimes used in choosing nominating committees.

May be amended and debated with restrictions. Both must refer to the motion to commit and not the main motion.

Take precedence over an amendment to the main motion and postpone indefinitely.

Cannot be used to commit any of the subsidiary motions.

Answers to the Eight Fundamental Questions.

Can it interrupt a speaker?	No
Does it require a second?	Yes
Is it debatable?	Yes
Is it amendable?	Yes
Is a vote required?	Majority
It only applies to what?	Amend and main motion
What can be applied to it?	Previous question
	Limit or extend debate
Is it renewable?	Yes

18—Amend—18

Purpose. To modify or change either slightly or substantially a pending motion so that the form in which it is voted on will express more satisfactorily the thinking of the entire membership.

Example.

Member: "Mr. Chairman," (wait for recognition) "I move that we amend the motion by" (You may add, strike out, insert words or phrases, or even substitute an entirely new motion).

Another Member: "Mr. Chairman, I second the motion."

Chairman: "It is moved and seconded that we amend the pending motion" (state exactly the type of amendment that was made and state motion with the amendment). "Is there any discussion on the amendment?" (Chairman must allow sufficient time for proper discussion.)

"Those in favor of the amendment" (repeat it) "say 'I'." (Wait for vote.)

"Those opposed say 'no'." (Check vote.)

If "I" vote has a majority: "The 'I's' have it and the amendment is carried. The question is now on the motion as amended." (State the motion as amended for discussion.)

If the "no's" have a majority: "The 'no's' have it and the motion on the amendment is lost."

The chairman then continues with the discussion of the original motion.

Points to Remember. An amendment may be again amended but only to the second degree. It is not correct to amend an amended amendment. It takes precedence only over the motion which is being amended.

The chairman must decide on whether amendments should be considered. His opinion, of course, is always subject to appeal.

If an amendment is tabled, referred to a committee, or postponed to a definite time, it has the same effect as if these motions were made on the main motion since that also is tabled, committed, or postponed.

Answers to the Eight Fundamental Questions.

Can it interrupt a speaker?	No
Does it require a second?	Yes
Is it debatable?	Yes
Is it amendable?	Yes
Is a vote required?	Majority

It only applies to what?	Variable motions
What can be applied to it?	Subsidiary motions
Is it renewable?	No

19—Postpone indefinitely—19

Purpose. To enable those opposed to the motion to have a test of strength without actually voting on the main motion. With this motion before the house they can continue to discuss the main motion and perhaps win more support.

Example.

Member: "Mr. Chairman," (wait for recognition) "I move to postpone consideration of this motion indefinitely."

Another Member: "Mr. Chairman, I second the motion."

Chairman: "It is moved and seconded that we postpone consideration of this motion indefinitely. Is there any discussion?" (Chairman must allow sufficient time for proper discussion.)

"Those in favor say 'I'." (Wait for vote.)

"Those opposed say 'no'." (Check vote.)

If "I" vote has majority: "The 'I's' have it and the motion to postpone indefinitely is carried." The motion that is postponed in this manner cannot be brought up again at the same meeting or session.

If "no" vote has a majority: "The 'no's' have it and the motion to postpone indefinitely is lost."

The discussion now continues on the main motion.

Points to Remember. It takes precedence over the main motion, and it opens the main motion to further discussion.

It applies only to main motions.

Previous question may be used as a defense to stop debate by those in favor of the main motion.

Answers to the Eight Fundamental Questions.

Can it interrupt a speaker?	No
Does it require a second?	Yes
Is it debatable?	Yes
Is it amendable?	No
Is a vote required?	Majority
It only applies to what?	Main motions
What can be applied to it?	Previous question
	Limit or extend debate
Is it renewable?	Yes

20—Main motion—20

Purpose. To present a proposition in a formal manner to an assembly for its consideration so that it can be discussed and acted upon.

Example.

Member: "Mr. Chairman," (wait for recognition) "I move that we hold our annual clambake on June 15th."

Another Member: "Mr. Chairman, I second the motion."

Chairman: "It is moved and seconded that we have our annual clambake on June 15th. Is there any discussion?" (Chairman must allow sufficient time for proper discussion.)

"Those in favor of the motion say 'I'." (Wait for vote.)

"Those opposed say 'no'." (Check vote.)

If "I" vote has a majority: "The 'I's' have it and the motion is carried." The chairman now directs the assembly to the next order of business.

If "no" vote has a majority: "The 'no's' have it and the motion is lost."

Chairman continues with the next item of business.

Points to Remember. Has no precedence over any other motion and it is not in order if any other motion is pending.

Main motion must be made:

(*a*) In the proper manner

(*b*) At the proper time.

(*c*) In the proper form

(*d*) Consistent with the purpose of the society

(*e*) Properly seconded

Proper manner: This means that the member rises, addresses the chair, and after recognition states his motion.

Proper time: Must be made when no other motion is pending.

Proper form: The motion must be stated in a clear manner so that the assembly will know what it is going to consider.

Consistent with the purpose of the society: It must be something connected directly with the purposes for which the society was formed.

Properly seconded: This is to assure that at least two members are in favor of having the matter considered.

Answers to the Eight Fundamental Questions.

Can it interrupt a speaker?   No

Does it require a second?   Yes

Is it debatable?   Yes
Is it amendable?   Yes
Is a vote required?   Majority
It only applies to what?   No motions
What can be applied to it?   Object to consideration
                                          All subsidiary motions
Is it renewable?   No

21—Reconsider—21

Purpose. To give the assembly an opportunity to correct an action taken in haste or an obvious mistake. Also to prevent a small group which happens to be a temporary majority from forcing the assembly to take an action which is irrevocable.

Example.

Member: "Mr. Chairman," (not waiting for recognition) "I move that we reconsider the vote on the motion" (state motion accurately).

Another Member: "Mr. Chairman, I second the motion."

Chairman: "It is moved and seconded that we reconsider the vote on the motion" (state the motion). "Is there any discussion?

"Those in favor of the motion to reconsider the motion say 'I'." (Wait for vote.)

"Those opposed say 'no'." (Check vote.)

If the "I" vote has a majority: "The 'I's' have it and the motion to reconsider is carried."

The chairman explains the motion which is to be reconsidered and asks if there is any discussion on it.

If the "no" vote has a majority: "The 'no's' have it and the motion to reconsider the vote on" (state motion) "is lost."

The chairman continues with the next order of business.

Points to Remember. No motion may be reconsidered twice.

Is in order at any time for the purpose of entry but not necessarily for discussion and vote.

May be moved by anyone regardless of which side he may have voted on originally.

If action that cannot be changed has already taken place as a result of the original vote, the motion is not in order.

It must be made on the same day or the next succeeding day after the vote to which it applies was taken.

It must be used with discretion since once it has been moved it stops all action on the motion to which it applies.

It is an appendage motion; therefore, it receives its precedence and its debatable or undebatable quality from the motion to which it applies.

So as not to make its application too complicated, it should be used only with appeal, amend, and main motions.

Motions to postpone definitely, previous question, and limit or extend debate may be applied to it.

Answers to the Eight Fundamental Questions.

Can it interrupt a speaker?	Yes
Does it require a second?	Yes
Is it debatable?	Yes
Is it amendable?	No
Is a vote required?	Majority
It only applies to what?	Appeal, amend, and main
What can be applied to it?	Previous question
	Limit or extend debate
	Postpone definitely
Is it renewable?	No

22—Rescind—22

Purpose. To repeal or annul the previous action of the assembly taken at the same meeting or at a previous meeting.

Example.

Member: "Mr. Chairman," (wait for recognition) "I move that we rescind the motion" (state the motion exactly as it was when previously acted upon).

Another Member: "Mr. Chairman, I second the motion."

Chairman: "It is moved and seconded that the assembly rescind the motion that" (repeat the motion in question). "Is there any discussion?" (Chairman must allow sufficient time for proper discussion.)

   "Those in favor of the motion to rescind say 'I'." (Wait for vote.)

   "Those opposed say 'no'." (Check vote.)

If "I" vote has two-thirds: "The 'I's' have it and the motion to rescind is carried.

   "The motion to" (repeat the motion in question) "is thereby rescinded. The secretary will please so note in the records." The chairman continues with the next order of business.

If "no" vote has one more than a third: "The 'no's' have it and the motion to rescind is lost." Normal business is continued.

Points to Remember. This motion is not in order if the motion to reconsider may be applied or if action taken as a result of the motion cannot be reversed.

May be used only on main motions. In order to put finality on motions after they have been voted on, it requires a two-thirds vote to rescind or repeal motions already properly considered.

Answers to the Eight Fundamental Questions.

Can it interrupt a speaker?	No
Does it require a second?	Yes
Is it debatable?	Yes
Is it amendable?	No
Is a vote required?	Two-thirds
It only applies to what?	Main motions
What can be applied to it?	All subsidiary
Is it renewable?	No

23—Take from table—23

Purpose. To allow the assembly to resume consideration of a motion previously laid on the table.

Example.

Member: "Mr. Chairman," (wait for recognition) "I move we take from the table" (state the motion exactly as it was when tabled).

Another Member: "Mr. Chairman, I second the motion."

Chairman: "It is moved and seconded that we take from the table" (repeat the tabled motion).

"Those in favor of taking this motion from the table say 'I'." (Wait for vote.)

"Those opposed say 'no'." (Check vote.)

If "I" vote has a majority: "The 'I's' have it and the motion to take from the table is carried. The motion you now have before the house is" (state the tabled motion). "Is there any discussion on this motion?"

If "no" vote has a majority: "The 'no's' have it and the motion to take from the table is lost."

The chairman leads the assembly into the next order of business.

Points to Remember. Take from the table may be made at the same meeting or the next regular meeting.

Has the same precedence as any main motion.

No other motions may be applied to it, but if the motion is taken from the table, it again functions as a main motion.

A motion must be taken from the table either at the meeting at which it was tabled or the next meeting, or it becomes null and void. This refers to societies that meet at least quarterly.

Answers to the Eight Fundamental Questions.

Can it interrupt a speaker?	No
Does it require a second?	Yes
Is it debatable?	No
Is it amendable?	No
Is a vote required?	Majority
It only applies to what?	Appeal, amend, or main motions
What can be applied to it?	No motions
Is it renewable?	Yes

Motions requiring special attention

The motions to amend and previous question present certain special problems; and, therefore, a more detailed explanation of how these motions function follows.

Amend. An amendment must be made so that its terminology will agree with the wording of the original motion. There are three ways to properly use the motion to amend:

1. Inserting
2. Striking out
3. Substituting a word, phrase, or even an entirely new motion

After the original motion has been amended by any one of these three methods, it is then stated by the chair with its amendment and again considered. At this stage the motion, even though amended, is still open for consideration as it was originally and may be amended again. If the vote on the amendment is lost, discussion on the original motion continues. Other amendments may be presented.

Remember there is no limit to the number of times a motion may be amended as long as not more than two amendments are on the floor at the same time.

While an amendment is being considered, another amendment cannot be made before the first one is disposed of unless it will alter the one under discussion. A second amendment must be a motion to change the first amendment.

Example.

a. Original motion: "I move that the club purchase a television set."

b. "I move to amend by inserting 'table model' before the word television."

c. "I move to amend by substituting 'console' for table model."

With these two amendments pending it would be out of order to:

1. Make a third amendment.

2. To propose to amend and substitute "combination" for "table model" in the first amendment. The second amendment must be disposed of before the first can be considered.

3. To propose to substitute "radio" for "television" in the original motion. The two amendments must be disposed of before the original motion may again be considered.

Amendments must be considered in the following sequence:

1. 2d amendment
2. 1st amendment
3. Original motion

Even though one or both of the amendments are carried, the original motion must be again put before the assembly as amended for its further consideration. At this time other amendments may be offered.

Previous Question. Because of the confusion in terminology it might be well to emphasize that this motion as it is used under our parliamentary system always means to stop debate and vote immediately.

When there is more than one motion before the house, the previous question may be moved on one or on all of the motions pending. Unless the purpose is specified, previous question applies only to the immediately pending motion.

Example:

1. "I move the club have its clambake on June 15th."

2. "I move to amend by substituting June 25th for June 15th."

3. "I move to refer this motion to a committee."

4. "I move to postpone consideration of this motion until our next meeting."

5. "I move the previous question on the motions to amend, commit, and postpone."

In this situation the following order should be followed:

a. If the vote on the previous question is in the affirmative (two-thirds vote), the motion to postpone must be voted on first.

b. If this motion is lost, then the motion to refer to a committee is voted on next.

c. If this motion is lost, then the motion to amend is voted on.

d. If this motion is lost, then the previous question is exhausted and the motion to have the clambake on June 15th is before the assembly for further discussion.

e. If the motion to postpone is voted in the affirmative, the question is temporarily disposed of, and obviously the motions to commit and amend would not be voted on.

f. If the motion to postpone is lost and the motion to commit carried, then the question, of course, would be committed. The motion to amend in this case would not be considered.

g. If the motion to commit is lost and the motion to amend carried, then the motion, as amended, that the club have the clambake on June 25th is presented to the assembly for its consideration.

If the vote on the previous question is lost the discussion continues as if the motion had never been made. The previous question is in order whenever a debatable motion is being considered.

14 Committees

INTRODUCTION

"Let's appoint a committee" is a phrase that is used by all organizations so often that it has become a by-word in our parliamentary way of living. It is estimated that the number of committees actually functioning in this country is in the millions. Most of us, unless we live as hermits, belong to one or several organizations and, as a result, are now or have been at one time members of some committee.

Why committees?

In order for an organization to accomplish the purpose of its existence, it must utilize the talents of all of its members. Part of the work may be done by individuals; part of it may be accomplished by the efforts of the entire organization. However, the most democratic and also the most practical way of getting things done is by utilizing small groups appointed to do a specific job, in other words, committees.

Advantages of appointing a committee

A committee may function more effectively than the larger organization because:

1. Informality gives all members more freedom to express their ideas.
2. Since usually no time limit is set, a more thorough discussion may be had.

3. Experts may be invited to express their views even though they are not members of the organization.
4. Members who would hesitate to express themselves before the large organization feel free to talk in the small informal group, particularly since strict adherence to rules of order are not followed.

How committees are created

An organization may have stipulated in the by-laws how committees shall be formed. The by-laws may also designate the function, authority, and the size of the committees. In order to handle the wide variety of business that comes up at every meeting specific motions to refer a matter to a committee are constantly being made. Committees of this type carry on the major part of the activities of any organization.

Duties of a committee chairman

The committee chairman who is appointed by the chairman of the larger organization when the committee was created should:

1. Participate actively as a leader in all discussions
2. Arrange a detailed agenda for all meetings
3. Assist in the preparation and drafting of the report to be presented to the organization

The committee report

The report should express the opinion of the majority. If a substantial difference of opinion exists among the committee members, the minority group should be allowed to present their report.

The majority report may be simply filed for information (as a financial report). It may be merely a progress report which does not require any action. It may be a report which ends up with a motion recommending certain action. This type of motion is handled the same as any other main motion.

Kinds of committees

Committees are generally classified as:

Standing
Special
Committee of the whole
Informal Committee

Standing Committees. These committees are considered "permanent" and last for the duration of the term of the chairman who appointed them. They are such committees as publicity, finance, nominating, and the like.

Special Committees. These committees are created to accomplish a definite, immediate purpose such as a Christmas party, annual clambake, etc. When the task has been completed, they are automatically disbanded. Most of the business of all organizations is handled by the work of these special committees.

Committee of the Whole. The purpose of this committee is to place a motion before the house for discussion free from restraints imposed upon it by the normal rules of order.

In a committee of the whole the chairman of the organization appoints the next ranking officer to take the chair and becomes an active member of the committee. When the motion to rise and report is passed, the chairman takes his normal place and the organization returns to regular procedure.

Informal Committee. This is much more flexible than committee of the whole and accomplishes the same objective. Technicalities are minimized and business is expedited. The chairman in the informal committee does not leave the chair and may participate actively in the discussion exactly the same as if he were chairman of a small committee.

Motions in committee of the whole and informal committee

In these committees, motions such as previous question or limit debate are out of order. Also motions to lay on the table, postpone, commit, and privileged motions are out of order. The only motion in order after the committee has reached a decision is to terminate the committee by the motion, "I move that the Committee rise and report."

If no decision has been reached in these committees, they may be terminated by a member moving, "the committee rise and report that it has had under its consideration such a motion but has reached no conclusion." Or if there has been a time limit on the committee, a member may move, "Since the time of adjournment has come, the committee will rise and report."

After the "rise and report" motion the organization immediately returns to normal parliamentary procedure and all informality should be terminated.

A committee has no authority to change a motion which it was appointed to consider. The committee may draw up a separate report to be presented to the assembly. However, the original motion must come back to the organization unchanged.

It is a good practice when the committee members have reached an agreement on their assigned task to formally move that this composite opinion be presented to the organization as the committee report.

15 *Rights of the Minority*

INTRODUCTION

The rights of the minority must always be protected, otherwise one of the basic purposes of parliamentary procedure will not be realized—equal rights to all members.

If the expression of the assembly is unanimous, there is no need for rules or procedure. If the majority favors a program, they, as a majority, are well taken care of. It is always the minority group that is in need of assistance.

A minority of one more than one-third may:

1. Prevent debate on a motion being stopped or even limited
2. Force a motion to be considered even though a motion objecting to its consideration was made and favored by a majority.
3. Prevent the suspension of a rule even though the majority favors it.

It is evident from the foregoing facts that a minority group does have power in an organization and may actually control many of its activities.

Strategy of the minority

If it is obvious that a motion you are opposed to is going to be carried, the first move is to take the necessary steps that will keep debate on the motion open until a majority may be won over to your side.

In order to accomplish this, use the following motions:

1. Move to recess. During this time canvassing the membership directly may prove helpful.
2. Move to lay on the table. Very often a motion laid on the table is never taken off.
3. Move to postpone indefinitely. This will serve two purposes; if it is carried it will kill the motion; if it is rejected it will at least give a test vote and show what support there is for and against the motion.
4. Move to refer to a committee. Besides gaining additional time you may be able to name your supporters as members of the committee.
5. Move to postpone to a definite time. This will give you an opportunity to win more support before the next meeting.

If the main motion in question is actually voted on and passed, there are two more strategic moves left:

a. Move to reconsider. This motion reopens the main motion to debate and stops all action resulting from the motion that was voted on.
b. Move to rescind. As a last resort if the motion to reconsider is lost, a motion to rescind (make null and void) may be made. This requires a two-thirds vote to void the original decision.

16 Organizations

INTRODUCTION

Organizations are of the following two kinds:

1. Temporary—created for a specific immediate purpose. When this purpose is accomplished the organization is automatically dissolved.
2. Permanent—created to function for a long time or indefinitely.

Forming a temporary organization

A gathering of this type is the same as a mass meeting and is kept as simple as possible. The interested group calls the meeting, explains the purpose of the gathering, and elects a temporary chairman and secretary, if necessary, to function for the life of the organization. This may be one or several meetings depending on the goal to be attained.

This type of organization might get together to discuss and draw up a resolution against, for example, high school taxes, endorsement of a certain political candidate, etc. When its purpose is accomplished it is automatically terminated.

Forming a permanent organization

The interested group secures a hall, notifies those whom they want to attend about the meeting, the time, its purposes, etc. When the meeting convenes, the first move is for one of the members to rise and say: "I move that Mr. Brown be elected temporary chairman. Is there a second?" Immediately when the temporary chairman takes over, he calls for nominations for the position of temporary secretary. After the secretary is elected the temporary organization is officially created.

The temporary chairman, Mr. Brown, now calls on the interested parties to explain why this new organization should be formed. When there has been sufficient discussion, a member should move that a permanent society be formed.

If the motion to form a permanent society is given an affirmative vote by a majority of the members then the next move is as follows:

1. To appoint (by the chairman) or elect a constitution and by-laws committee
2. To appoint (by the chairman) or elect a nominating committee to select a slate of permanent officers to be presented at the next meeting.

At the next meeting the first order of business is the consideration of the constitution and by-laws. After these have been approved, the nominating committee reports; and the election of officers takes place in the usual manner.

Constitution

The constitution should include:

Article I: Name of organization
Article II: Purpose and powers of the organization
Article III: Membership
Article IV: Officers
Article V: Governing board, executive board, or board of trustees
Article VI: Meetings
Article VII: Quorum
Article VIII: Method of amending constitution

A preamble may be used as a preface to the constitution and should contain the reason for the formation of the organization.

By-laws

The by-laws are, in effect, a detailed explanation of the constitution, such as:

1. Kinds of members
2. Duties of officers, etc.

Officers

The two most important officers are the president and secretary.

President. The president of a society should have two essential qualifications:

1. He should be an outstanding leader
2. He should have the ability to preside over a meeting in a competent, efficient manner

Secretary. The principal duties of a secretary are:

1. To keep accurate records of all the proceedings of the meetings
2. To have all the necessary records available at all times, such as:
   a. List of names of members
   b. List of names of all committees and their members
   c. Copy of constitution and by-laws
   d. Copy of all essential papers that are to be read at the meeting
   e. Copy of the order of business so as to assist the chairman
3. To take care of all necessary correspondence for the society

The minutes of a meeting should include the following:

1. Name of organization.
2. Statement of whether the meeting was "regular," "special," etc.
3. Date, time, and place.
4. Who presided.
5. How the minutes of the previous meeting were read and disposed of.
6. What committee reports were made.
7. Accurate record of main motions and how they were disposed of. There is no need to record any debate or discussion on a motion.

Order of business

The order of business is as follows:

1. Call to order
2. Reading of minutes
3. Committee reports
4. Unfinished business
5. New business
6. Special announcements
7. Adjournment

Table 16-1

Order of precedence	Can it interrupt a speaker?	Does it require a second?	Is it debatable?	Is it amendable?	Is a vote required?	It only applies to what?	What can be applied to it?	Is it renewable?
I Privileged motions								
1. Adjourn	No	Yes	No	No	Majority	No motion	No motion	Yes[2]
2. Recess	No	Yes	No	Yes[1]	Majority	No motion	Amend[1]	Yes[2]
3. Question of privilege	Yes	No	No	No	No vote	No motion	No motion	No
II Incidental motions								
4. Orders of the day	Yes	No	No	No	No vote	No motion	No motion	No
5. Point of order	Yes	No	No	No	No vote	Any error	No motion	No
6. Appeal	Yes	Yes	No	No	Tie or majority	Decisions of chair	13, 14, 15, 16	No
7. Suspension of rules	No	Yes	No	No	Two-thirds	No motion	No motion	Yes[2]
8. Object of consideration	Yes	No	No	No	Two-thirds	Main motion	No motion	No
9. Information	Yes	No	No	No	No vote	No motion	No motion	No
10. Withdraw a motion	No	No	No	No	Majority	All motions	No motion	Yes[2]
11. Division of question	No	No	No	No	No vote	Main, amend	No motion	No
12. Division of assembly	Yes	No	No	No	No vote	Voice votes	No motion	No

III Subsidiary motions

13. Lay on the table (postpone temporarily)	No	Yes	No	No	Majority	Main, amend, appeal	No motion	Yes²
14. Previous question (vote immediately)	No	Yes	No	No	Two-thirds	Debatable motions	No motion	Yes²
15. Limit or extend debate	No	Yes	No	Yes	Two-thirds	Debatable motions	Amend¹	Yes²
16. Postpone definitely	No	Yes	Yes¹	Yes¹	Majority	Main motion	14, 15, 18	Yes²
17. Refer to committee	No	Yes	Yes¹	Yes¹	Majority	Main, amend	14, 15, 18	Yes²
18. Amend	No	Yes	Yes	Yes	Majority	Variable in form	Subsidiary motions	No
19. Postpone indefinitely	No	Yes	Yes	No	Majority	Main motion	14, 15	No

IV Main motions

20. Main	No	Yes	Yes	Yes	Majority	No motion	Subsidiary, 8	No
21. Reconsider	Yes	Yes	Yes	No	Majority	Main, amend, appeal	14, 15, 16	No
22. Rescind	No	Yes	Yes	No	Two-thirds	Main motion	Subsidiary motions	No
23. Take from table	No	Yes	No	No	Majority	Main, amend, appeal	No motion	Yes²
24. Create orders	No	Yes	Yes¹	Yes¹	Majority	Main	Amend	Yes²

1 Restricted to motion itself.
2 After progress in business of meeting.

Index